THERE'S ADVENTURE
IN
JET AIRCRAFT

commercial pilot

aerodynamic engineering

military pilot

propulsion engineering

test pilot

aircraft design

There's Adventure in

JET
AIRCRAFT

by Julian May

Illustrated by
Robert Barker

POPULAR MECHANICS PRESS

Chicago

To Davo,
the most junior birdman

ACKNOWLEDGMENTS

THE AUTHOR'S THANKS are due to the many aviation people, both civil and military, who made this book possible: *At the Dept. of the Air Force:* Maj. James F. Sunderman, Maj. Tim Dunn. *At AFFTC, Edwards AFB, Calif.:* Maj. Ruth M. Dudley, Capt. Joe B. Jordan, Mr. Marion I. Kent. *At AFMDC, Holloman AFB, N.M.:* Lt. Col. and Mrs. Rufus R. Hessberg, Jr., Lt. Col. Donald H. Vlcek, Lt. Virgil V. Dominic, Mr. and Mrs. George Meeter. *At WADC, Wright-Patterson AFB, Ohio:* Mr. Lewis Zarem, Mr. C. Carroll High, Jr., Mr. B. T. Wolfson, 1st Lt. Robert N. Olson, Dr. Edward Vail, Dr. Ray Kline. *At Truax Field, Madison Wisc.:* Capt. Harry Scarborough, 1st Lt. Leslie C. Conwell. *Civil Air Patrol:* Lt. Col. Raymond Johnson, Col. J. Gibbs Spring, Maj. Gerald Whaley, W/O Steve Kimmell. *At Boeing Airplane Co., Seattle, Wash.:* Mr. Robert S. Mansfield, Mr. Gordon Williams. *At Cessna Aircraft Co., Wichita, Kans.:* Mr. Bill Robinson, Mr. R. L. Griesinger.

Special thanks are due to Capt. Edward C. Christman, Base Operations Officer, 327th FGRU, Truax Field, for his nonchalance during the author's attempts to fly a T-33; and to Sgt. Bill Wallrich for his special help and for permission to quote two songs from his book, *Air Force Airs,* published by Duell, Sloane & Pearce.

Chicago, Illinois   J.M.

Other Books in the Series:

THERE'S ADVENTURE IN ATOMIC ENERGY

THERE'S ADVENTURE IN CHEMISTRY

THERE'S ADVENTURE IN ELECTRONICS

THERE'S ADVENTURE IN ROCKETS

THERE'S ADVENTURE IN METEOROLOGY

THERE'S ADVENTURE IN CIVIL ENGINEERING

THERE'S ADVENTURE IN GEOLOGY

THERE'S ADVENTURE IN MARINE SCIENCE

CONTENTS

Chapter   *Page*
1   Jets Across America   13

2   The Flying Cattleman   30

3   Air-Age Cadets   50

4   Western-Style Wings   62

5   Beyond Sound   87

6   At The Controls   107

7   Speed Limit — 3,000 M.P.H.   122

8   Redcap   146

9   The Opening Skies   163

PREFACE

TO THE READER:

The events in this book are fiction, but the Civil Air Patrol is a real organization that introduces the world of aviation to boys and girls of high school age. If *you* are interested in joining, call your local airport and inquire about CAP cadet activities.

CAP offers a jet orientation course to outstanding cadets, and its members also participate in other exciting aviation activities. It should be understood, however, that CAP does not offer free flying lessons; it does not compete with those who make a living by giving flight instruction.

During times of emergency, the duties of CAP cadets include manning radios and giving vital ground support to aircraft. Although cadet observers have participated in hazardous search-and-rescue missions under extraordinary circumstances, the boys and girls are not ordinarily permitted to fly in the search planes. It is too dangerous. Randy Morrow's role in the search-and-rescue mission described in this book has been included for the sake of dramatic impact; but it should not be thought of as typical.

J.M.

FOREWORD

AVIATION AND YOUTH go together as naturally as birds and flight. No field of activity challenges the youthful imagination or evokes an emotion of such thrilling achievement as aviation. Those of you who, like Randy Morrow, are just beginning to fly know this. Those who are looking forward to their first flying experience have this great treat in store for them.

Aviation is the youngest, most vigorous, rapidly developing science — and force — the world has ever known. Aviation's entire development has taken place within the span of your father's or grandfather's lifetime. It was on December 17, 1903, that the Wright Brothers solved the mystery of powered flight at Kitty Hawk. The flight lasted only 12 seconds and covered a distance of only 120 feet but it marked the beginning of a new age for man. True, the tremendous significance of the Wrights' discovery was not recognized at the time, but the impact the "flying machine" made on man's world was felt soon enough. It heralded the beginning of a fantastic age of technological progress.

Thirty years after Lindbergh began his historic flight to

Paris on May 20, 1927, a USAF F-100 jet aircraft followed the same route as the "Spirit of St. Louis" and cut Lindbergh's time of 33 hours and 30 minutes to 6 hours and 35 minutes.

Today the civil jet age is just beginning. Before long you will be able to leave Paris at 11 A.M. and arrive in New York at 7:30 A.M.! You will have covered a distance of 3200 nautical miles in 150 minutes!

The Civil Air Patrol cadet program is filled with a variety of activities designed to introduce you to the world of aviation and give you an insight into the effects aviation has on our society. A cadet is given opportunities to attend encampments at military bases; participate in the International Air Cadet Exchange program with young men from 21 other nations; take orientation flights in military and civil aircraft; participate in drill competitions; and, if he is lucky, attend the CAP Jet Orientation Course where he actually gets a chance to handle the controls of a T-33 jet trainer.

Those young men who contemplate a life of military service will find their CAP experiences to be good preparation. Over 10 per cent of the first USAF Academy class, graduated on June 3, 1959, had their start in Civil Air Patrol. Many more former CAP cadets are now in training at the Academy and in the regular Air Force. CAP training also offers many challenging experiences that will help prepare you for profitable career possibilities in civil aviation.

Above all, the CAP cadet program helps prepare our American youth to become useful and productive citizens. The nation looks to its youth to solve the new and complex problems of society. Youth is our most precious commodity. Yet youth will face the mighty challenge of the Aerospace Age ahead with a sense of achievement and

adventure. Today's youth has before it the greatest
opportunity in human history, as well as the responsibility,
to lead the world to peace and universal understanding.

STEPHEN D. McELROY
Brigadier General, USAF
National Commander
Civil Air Patrol

National Headquarters
Civil Air Patrol
Auxiliary of the United States Air Force
Bolling Air Force Base 25, D.C.

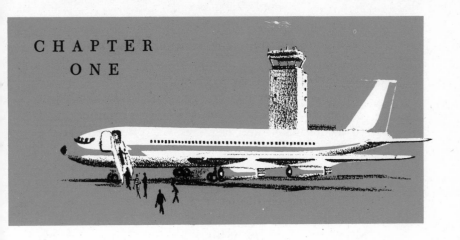

CHAPTER
ONE

JETS ACROSS AMERICA

As THE TAXI pulled up in front of the terminal building of O'Hare Field, Chicago International Airport, Randy Morrow heard the sound.

It was something like a bellow, and something like a whining scream. He had never heard anything like it before. Not that the sound was extremely loud — it was just *different*.

"That's our jet!" said Sam, Randy's younger brother, "I'll bet my last nickel on it! That's the jet we're going to ride!"

Randy glanced questioningly at his father as they got out of the taxi. "How about it, Dad? Is that the 707?"

13

"Sounds like a multi-engine jet of some kind," Mr. Morrow agreed.

Sam exclaimed, "I want to see it!"

The boys' mother had a suggestion. "Why don't you go up onto the observation deck while your father and I attend to the tickets and baggage? We'll meet you at the gate in ten minutes."

"Swell, Mom!" Sam took off at breakneck speed.

"What an eager beaver," Randy said, shaking his head. "He'll be riding on the jet in a half hour or so, but he still can't wait to get a look at it."

Mr. Morrow winked at his older son. "Remember that you were a beaver yourself once. Go keep an eye on him."

A sign directed Randy to the observation deck that overlooked the big airfield. He found Sam there, leaning over the railing, staring in open-mouthed awe at the ships on the field below.

"O'Hare is a pretty big place," Randy remarked, taking a place at his brother's side.

"There's the 707," Sam said, pointing. Randy saw a huge silver ship with a red stripe down its side, on its engine housings, and on its wing and tail control surfaces. It was much longer than the largest piston-engine plane on the field, and seemed to squat closer to the ramp than the other planes did.

"Quite a ship," Randy said admiringly. "I hear she needs a pretty long runway to take off on."

"Big jets need about 8,000 feet," said a voice behind the boys. It was a cockney voice, and when Sam and Randy turned around, they found that it belonged to a little man with one of the most remarkable faces they had ever seen. It was deep bronze in color, criss-crossed with thousands of tiny lines that looked almost like roadways

"Will you look at that, chaps?"

on a map. The eyes, peering from beneath bristling sandy brows, were a startling bright blue. The little man wore an old tan trenchcoat and a cloth cap.

"And that's why you can't make a jet terminal out of just *any* old aerodrome. In a pinch, a jet can land on almost any commercial field. But 'ere's the rub—she can't take off again with 'er load unless she's got more than 7,000 feet to run on."

Sam said, "Well — Dad told us that this airport is specially set up for jets!"

"You're right, nipper. And many's the one I've seen 'ere. Watchin' 'em is by way of bein' my 'obby, you might say. Now that my old ticker ain't what she used to be, the bloomin' FAA took my pilot's certificate away from me—"

"You were a pilot?" Sam asked.

"Was I a pilot—? Just a flight leftenant in the R.A.F., that's all! Why I was even at Cranwell Aerodrome the day Whittle's E28/39 took off for the first time."

"Whittle," Randy mused. Then his eyebrows shot up. "You mean Frank Whittle, the man who invented the first successful jet plane?"

The little man bobbed his head in assent. "The same! It was back in 1941, a wretched day in May with a ceiling about as 'igh as your 'at. Me and the rest of the blokes was standin' around 'opin' the clouds would lift so's we could 'ave another go at Jerry.

"Whittle and 'is crew had their plane in one of the 'angars. Secret like. They 'ad all of us curious as cats, wonderin' what a jet engine might be. Wasn't a one of us thought that engine'd lift a ship off the tarmac."

The little man's eyes narrowed and he smiled in reminiscence, looking out over the expanse of O'Hare. Randy

"You were a pilot?" Sam asked..

thought, what a difference there must be between this busy American air terminal and the English R.A.F. station where the first jet flew.

"Finally the clouds broke," the little man said. "Whittle's men brought out the E28/39—and a measly little toy of a thing she was, I'll tell you! 'Lor' lum and blimey!' yells Thrombey, one of the Spitfire pilots. 'Will you look at that, chaps? *No propeller!*'

"Whittle's test pilot was Gerry Sayer. He got into the little monstrosity after they trundled it out onto the runway, fired 'er up, and tested the engine. She yowled, and she roared, and then Sayer let loose the brake. Away she went, while we all stood there with our jaws flappin'.

"We could 'ear 'er upstairs behind the clouds—nothin' else made a sound like that!—but we didn't see 'er again until she circled in for a landing. Sayer gave us the thumbs-up sign, and we all cheered. But Thrombey says to us, 'That's a real novelty Whittle's got there. But it'll never be practical. Who wants to trust 'is life to a bloomin' blowtorch?' "

The little ex-pilot smiled wryly and shoved his hands into the pockets of his trenchcoat. "None of us saw very far into the future in those days, I'm afraid."

"When I grow up," Sam announced, "I'm going to fly a jet."

"I envy you. Lord knows I envy you," said the Englishman.

A loudspeaker nearby burst out, "American Airlines Flight 672, the Los Angeles Jet Flagship, is now boarding passengers at Gate 28. All aboard, please."

"That's our plane," said Randy.

"So long, mister," Sam said, and dashed for the stairway.

18

Randy said, "Thank you for telling us about Whittle's jet, sir."

"My pleasure. Have a good flight, and good-bye."

"Good-bye—Lieutenant."

The little man's shoulders straightened and his chin lifted. He winked at Randy.

Randy winked back.

The boys found their parents standing apart from the group of passengers at the gate. With Mr. and Mrs. Morrow was a man who wore the blue uniform and cap of an airline pilot.

"Captain Simmons, these are our boys, Randy and Sam," said Mr. Morrow. "Boys, meet Captain Simmons. He'll be piloting our 707 to Los Angeles."

The pilot shook hands with the boys. "Your dad's been telling me about the science books and articles that he writes. Sounds like a mighty interesting way to make a living."

"I'd like to do what *you* do," Sam declared.

The captain laughed. "It's fun, all right. But remember that there's work in it, too. I've been flying for more than twenty years."

Mr. Morrow said, "Captain Simmons flew piston-engine planes throughout most of his career, boys. He got his jet training within the last two years."

"Is a jet very different from a regular plane?" asked Randy.

"Suppose we go out on the ramp and look our ship over," the captain suggested.

The jet had looked big from the observation deck, but seen from the ground, it was tremendous. Captain Simmons told Randy that the Boeing 707 was over 144 feet long, and had a wingspan of more than 130 feet. The wings were swept back and had been designed to flex slightly in rough air to cushion the effect of "air bumps."

"Why do the wings sweep back?" Randy asked.

"Well, aerodynamic engineers have found that swept wings cut through the air more easily at speeds near that of sound. Actually, you could get somewhat the same effect by making straight wings very thin. Military jets do this. But a transport carries its fuel in wing tanks, so the thin-wing alternative is out."

"I see," said Randy. "Can we get a closer look at the engines?"

"Certainly." They walked up to the plane. The engines were suspended under the wing and forward of its leading edge. Captain Simmons called the engine's housing its *pod*.

"The 707 has four Pratt and Whitney JT3C-6 turbojet engines," he said. "You boys know how a turbojet works?"

They shook their heads.

"Well, the engine is open at both ends. Air comes in through the intake at the front. It's squeezed together by fanlike compressor blades. The compressed air goes to metal combustion chambers where the fuel is injected. Fuel and air mix and burn, and the hot exhaust gases rush out through the tailpipe. On the way out, the gases turn a turbine, which is connected by a shaft to the compressor up front."

"But where does the power come from?" Sam asked. "I mean, what makes the plane *move?*"

"A jet engine is a reaction engine. You know that for every action there's an equal and opposite reaction. A gun's recoil is reaction. Reaction is what makes a bal-

20

loon zoom around the room if you blow it up, then suddenly let it go so that the air squirts out of the open end."

"Sure," said Sam. "And doesn't a rocket work the same way?"

"It certainly does. Thrust in both rocket and jet engines comes from expanding exhaust gases. Of course the turbojet is just one kind of jet engine. The ramjet is another. It doesn't have any fan or turbine. Air is compressed in the engine as the ship moves through the air."

Captain Simmons went on to explain that ramjets would not operate if the plane was standing still. First the ship had to reach a speed of 200 miles per hour or more. At this speed, the air was "rammed" down the air intake and compressed. Fuel was injected, and the hot gases from the burning fuel were led out through the exhaust nozzle. The faster a ramjet went, the more efficient it became.

Mr. Morrow said, "Ramjets have been used in experimental aircraft, boys, and they've been used to power some winged missiles. But let's face it—an engine that requires a 200-mile-an-hour shove is not going to be too practical when it's used by itself. Ramjet craft are either launched from a fast-moving mother plane, or else they have auxiliary motors to get them started."

"I guess the ramjet isn't much good then," Randy remarked.

"Whoa!" laughed Mr. Morrow. "I didn't say that. As a single power plant, it's impractical. But it *is* used in the fastest jets. Ever hear of an afterburner?"

Randy frowned. "I've heard of it . . ."

"It's nothing but a ramjet stuck into the tailpipe of a turbojet. The engineers found that not all of the air was used in the turbojet's combustion chamber. So they

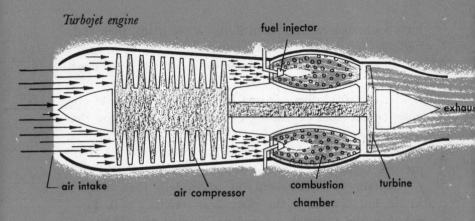

Turbojet engine

fuel injector

exhau⟩

air intake

air compressor

combustion chamber

turbine

Air entering the engine intake is compressed by the compressor blades and discharged into the combustion chambers. Fuel is injected, mixed with air, and ignited. Hot exhaust gases stream out the tailpipe. They strike the turbine, causing it to rotate and drive the compressor by means of a connecting shaft. Only part of the exhaust-gas energy is used to operate the turbine. The rest of the energy is transformed into forward thrust.

got the idea of injecting *more* fuel into the tailpipe, igniting this, and getting a bonus burst of thrust."

"Neat!" said Sam.

"Afterburners almost double the thrust of a turbojet engine," Captain Simmons continued. "But a pilot isn't going to use one all the time. Jets use enough fuel as it is! Afterburners are used only to give an extra burst of power when it's needed. This might be at takeoff, for example, if the pilot wanted to gain altitude quickly."

"Would the ramjet work then?" Randy puzzled. "The ship isn't moving very fast at takeoff."

"The ship isn't—the flowing gases in the tailpipe *are!*"

Randy smacked his forehead with his hand. "Sure! What a dummy I am!"

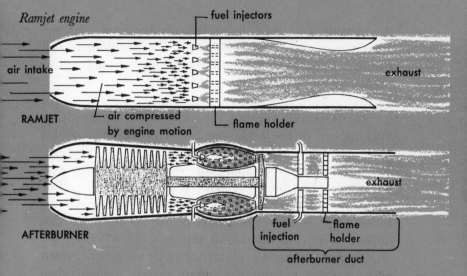

Ramjet engine

fuel injectors

air intake

exhaust

RAMJET

air compressed
by engine motion

flame holder

exhaust

AFTERBURNER

fuel
injection

flame
holder

afterburner duct

Ramjet compresses air by its own motion. Afterburner is ramjet assembly placed in tailpipe of turbojet. Additional fuel is injected, ignited, to give more thrust.

"Does the 707 have afterburners?" Mrs. Morrow asked.

"No, ma'am," said the captain. "They're used on combat aircraft. They're a little—uh—violent for passenger comfort. But the 707 does have another kind of system for increasing engine power. It's called water injection. The plane carries 700 gallons of purified water. When we take off, the water is injected into the compressor section of the engine to give added thrust."

Mrs. Morrow looked surprised. "But wouldn't that put the engine's flame out?"

The captain shook his head. "No—by the time the water is injected, the flame is too hot to be put out. What the water does is supply extra mass to be thrown out by the exhaust blast. And the more mass you throw out, the greater the thrust. This plane needs extra thrust at takeoff just to get it moving. Those 700 gallons of water are used up in two and a half minutes!"

"Wow!" exclaimed Sam.

Randy was inspecting the rear of the engine pod. Sticking out of the back was a device that resembled a cluster of organ pipes. "What's this?"

"That's the sound suppressor. You probably know that jet engines are about the noisiest things on earth. The sound from these babies would deafen you if it weren't toned down. So the engineers at Boeing spent ten million dollars to develop this sound suppressor."

Captain Simmons explained that jet noise was caused when the hot exhaust gas stream mixed suddenly and turbulently with the cooler air outside. Experiments showed that the sound could be reduced if the big exhaust stream were broken down into several smaller streams. The 707's sound suppressor had 21 specially designed tubes that did the work with a thrust loss of only 2½ per cent.

Mrs. Morrow said, "The jet we heard as we drove up to the airport *still* sounded pretty loud."

"Excuse me for contradicting you, ma'am," the pilot said, "but a 707 actually makes less noise on takeoff than the piston engine plane does! The sound is more high-pitched than a piston engine sound, though, and it does take some getting used to!"

Captain Simmons glanced at his watch. "Just about takeoff time, folks. We'd better get aboard."

The 707 was divided into two sections. There were 56 seats in the forward first-class section, and 56 aft in the tourist-class section. Each section had its own entrance, its own stewardesses, and its own facilities.

24

"That's the sound suppressor."

One of the first things the Morrows noticed was the unique use of color and decoration in the jetliner. The cabin was more beautiful than any they had ever seen.

"Comfortable seats, too!" Randy said approvingly, as he plumped down in his. The seats were much wider than those in conventional airliners, and there was a table between the window and aisle seats. The windows themselves were smaller than those in piston airliners, but there were more of them.

One of the stewardesses explained the passenger service unit, fitted below the hatrack over each row of seats. The unit contained reading lights, fresh-air outlets, and stewardess call buttons, as well as a NO SMOKING—FASTEN SEAT BELTS sign. Alternate units had loudspeakers for announcements or tape-recorded music.

"Music?" Mrs. Morrow inquired. "In the planes I've been in, you'd be lucky to hear the person next to you —much less any music!"

The stewardess smiled. "You have a surprise in store for you. There's no loud noise or vibration in a jetliner."

She said that the plane would cruise at 40,000 feet. Pressurization would maintain a cabin altitude of 8,000 feet.

"If the cabin pressure should fail for any reason, a door in the passenger service unit would open automatically and an oxygen mask would drop down right in front of you, ready for use." She demonstrated the oxygen supply. The mask was like a soft sponge-rubber box with a plastic bag attached. A line led from the plastic bag to the ship's oxygen bottles, stowed in the cargo hold.

"We're nearly ready now," the stewardess added. And sure enough, in a few minutes the voice of Captain Simmons came over the intercom, welcoming the passengers aboard and introducing the crew members.

26

"It is now 8.30 A.M. We are scheduled to arrive in Los Angeles at 10.30 A.M."

"It takes *two hours* for us to get from Chicago to Los Angeles?" Sam yelped incredulously.

"Remember the time lag, son," Mr. Morrow said. "Our trip takes four hours, but Los Angeles is two hours behind us."

"Boy, if this plane was any faster, we'd get there before we left!" Randy said.

The jet engines were turned on. Inside the sound-proofed cabin, the Morrows heard only a whining sound. There was no warm-up period. The plane moved to the far end of the runway, then began its takeoff. Randy noticed that it seemed to stay on the ground for a long time, but that once it did become airborne, it climbed rapidly. It was only minutes before they attained their cruising altitude.

Randy looked down. He had been in airliners many times before, since Mr. Morrow's work as a science writer made it necessary for the family to travel frequently. But Randy had never flown so high before. The earth beneath actually looked *curved!* Most of the surface features seemed to fade away. When he looked back, Randy could see the Great Lakes. Ahead of him stretched Illinois, Iowa, and Missouri.

There was a sound of money dropping on the table that separated Randy's seat from that of his brother.

"Darn," said Sam disgustedly. "It won't stand up."

"What won't stand up?" Randy asked.

"This cotton-pickin' half-dollar. In the articles you read about the jetliners, somebody's always balancing half-dollars on edge to show how steady and vibrationless the ship is. But it doesn't work!"

"Let's see that half-dollar," Randy ordered. He ex-

"Jets are sure great!"

amined the coin and snorted. "A 1922 half-dollar—almost as thin as paper! You double-dummkopf, this thing wouldn't stand on edge if you balanced it on the Rock of Gibraltar."

Mr. Morrow leaned across the aisle and held out another coin. "Try this new one, Sam."

The boy carefully set it on edge. It balanced perfectly. Sam sighed, settled back, and watched it with a look of peaceful fulfillment. "Jets sure are great," he said.

Randy said to his father, "I sure wish we could see the military jets that you're going to see, Dad."

"Sorry, Randy. The Air Force Flight Test Center at Edwards is usually off-limits to visitors. I can get in to gather material for my book—but no kibitzers allowed."

"We're going to have a great time at Uncle Glarfie's ranch," Sam said. "What's the name of the place, Mom?"

"The Flying X," said Mrs. Morrow. Garfield Haines, alias Uncle Glarfie, was her eldest brother. The boys had never met him.

"The Flying X," Sam repeated. "Gee!"

But Randy looked gloomy. "That horseflesh is going to fly mighty slow compared to this jet."

Mrs. Morrow smiled secretively. "You'll find that your uncle doesn't live *entirely* in the covered wagon era."

"What d'you mean, Mom?" Randy asked.

But Mrs. Morrow would say no more.

CHAPTER TWO

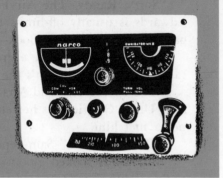

THE FLYING CATTLEMAN

"THERE'S LOS ANGELES," said Sam. The 707 banked around the sprawling California city and began to descend. "They must've known we were coming and turned the smog off!"

The big ship seemed to drop rapidly. Then, as they neared the runway, there was an abrupt decrease in speed. Mr. Morrow explained that the plane was being braked by flaplike devices on the wings, called "spoilers" because they spoiled the lift of the wing.

"We're down," said Randy. Suddenly there was a blast of power from the engines. Surprisingly enough, it seemed to slow the plane down.

"Thrust reversers," explained Mr. Morrow. "They're installed just forward of the sound suppressors. The pilot cuts them in when the ship lands, then gives 'er the gun. The reversers direct part of the thrust *forward* and help to brake the plane."

The jet taxied up to the terminal apron, then came to a final halt. The Morrows unfastened their seat belts and prepared to disembark.

"You boys might be interested in seeing another kind of commercial jet," said Mr. Morrow. "I think I see a Douglas DC-8 out there on the apron."

The boys peered around as they emerged into the California sunshine. There was a big crowd waiting at the gate.

"Barbara! Ken!" A very loud voice rang out. The owner of the voice, a tall man in a pale tan Stetson and brown cord suit, pushed toward the Morrows.

"Glarfie!" cried Mrs. Morrow. Her brother gave her an enthusiastic hug, then wrung Mr. Morrow's hand. Mrs. Morrow said, "Glar, I want you to meet our boys, Randy and Sam."

"Welcome to the West. I hope you're going to enjoy your stay at the Flying X. Dana's home on leave, and he and Carlos have been making a lot of plans that include you."

"My goodness, Glar," Mrs. Morrow said, "I forgot how big your boys must be by now."

"Carlos is sixteen—about the same as you, eh, Randy? And Dana's nineteen."

They moved to the baggage counter. Mr. Morrow said, "You must be pretty proud of Dana, Glar. It's quite an honor for a young man to become a cadet at the Air Force Academy."

"I can hardly wait to meet him," Sam exclaimed.

"We'll be at the Flying X inside of a few hours," his uncle said.

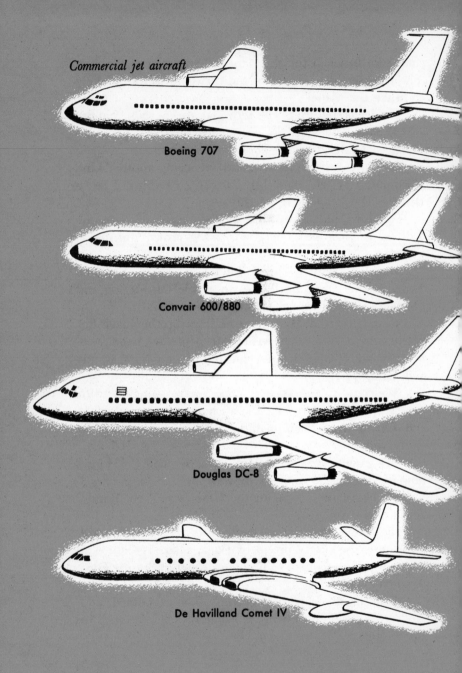

Commercial jet aircraft

Boeing 707

Convair 600/880

Douglas DC-8

De Havilland Comet IV

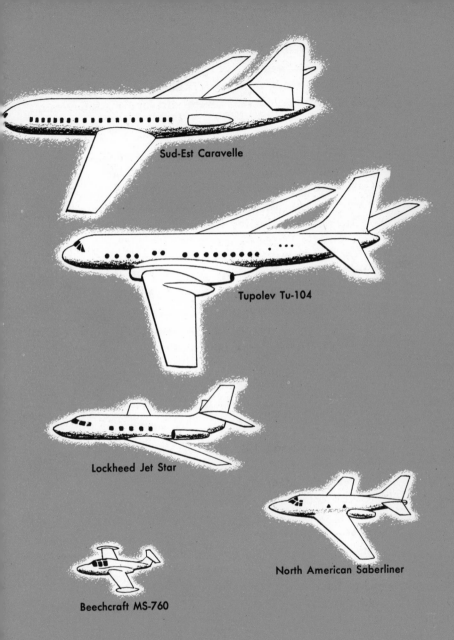

Sud-Est Caravelle

Tupolev Tu-104

Lockheed Jet Star

North American Saberliner

Beechcraft MS-760

"Here's our baggage," Mr. Morrow said. "We'll divide it up and get ready to separate. Glar, you probably know that I'm planning to visit several airplane manufacturers and Edwards Air Force Base before I come out to the ranch."

"Take your time," said the cattleman genially. "We'll expect you when we hear from you. Just fly into Santa Fe and give us a call. We'll pick you up."

Mr. Morrow got into a cab and headed for downtown Los Angeles. After seeing their father off, the boys asked Uncle Glarfie where his car was.

"Car?" the rancher asked.

"Well, Mom said you'd be taking us to the ranch."

"It's almost 800 miles to Cornudo, Randy. A long, hot trip by car! We're going another way." He led the boys and their mother out of the terminal building toward a part of the airport where light planes were parked.

Sam drew in his breath and his eyes widened. "We're going to fly in *your airplane?*"

"Right! It'd take two days to drive to the ranch. We'll fly there in about seven hours."

They began to stow the bags inside the plane. It was a four-place Cessna 175, painted black and white, with the Flying X brand on the cabin door.

"Let's go!" Sam said excitedly.

"Not so fast," his uncle said. "We've got something to take care of before we leave. Flying is different from driving. You usually don't just jump in to your plane and zoom off."

The rancher explained that the first thing a pilot did was to have his plane checked and fueled. This had already been done. Then he planned his course, using aeronautical charts.

"We're going to fly in your airplane?"

"I think you boys will be interested in these. They're quite different from road maps. Suppose you all climb in the ship—Barbara, would you and Sam like to sit in back? —and you can look at some of the charts while I get the weather report and file a flight plan."

"What's a flight plan, Uncle Glarfie?" Randy asked.

His uncle showed him a form with space for the plane's identification number, color, and make; the pilot's name; the altitudes and course the plane would follow; the destination and estimated time of arrival; and many other items of information.

"We don't really have to file a flight plan, since we're flying on VFR—that's Visual Flight Rules. If we were going to fly on instruments, we'd be required to file a plan."

"What's the flight plan used for?" Sam asked.

"Among other things, it helps the FAA to determine whether aircraft have been lost. That's why we're filing a plan, even though we don't have to. If we fail to file an arrival report within one hour of the estimated time of arrival at our destination, they'll start a search for us. If we haven't reported within three hours, the full facilities of the search-and-rescue service will be activated. Most pilots who do flying over rugged, desolate country file flight plans. It's only common sense."

Randy examined the charts after his uncle had gone. They were topographical, showing the elevation of the terrain by means of color bands and contour lines. Mountains, deserts, swamps, lakes, and rivers were prominently marked, as were other natural features that might be readily identified from the air. Other features such as railroad lines, bridges, tunnels, race tracks, oil derricks, mines, and ranches were also indicated. Airports were

A pilot's flight plan

U. S. DEPARTMENT OF COMMERCE—CIVIL AERONAUTICS ADMINISTRATION

FLIGHT PLAN

Form Approved
Budget Bureau No 41–R073.3

1. Type of Flight Plan	2. Aircraft Identification No.	3. Aircraft Type (If formation flights give types and number of aircraft.)	4. Estimated True Air Speed	5. Point of Departure
☒ IFR ☐ DVFR ☐ VFR	N31179	CESSNA 175	130 MPH Knots	LAX

6. Cruising Altitude and Route of Flight
80/V210 – V12 //INW// 90 – V12 – V60 – V190// VFR–FLYGX

7. Destination	8. Intermediate Stops	9. Departure Time		10. Estimated Elapsed Time*	
FLYING X (PVT) N.M.	INW	Proposed 1040 P	Actual —	Hours 3	Minutes 25

11. Alternate Airport	12. Fuel on Board		13. Radio Equipment (Circle applicable items)		14. Pilot's or Flight Commander's Name
LVS	Hours 5	Minutes 30	Transmitting HF (VHF) UHF None	Receiving (LF) VHF UHF None	G. B. HAINES

15. Remarks
3 PASSENGERS

16. Pilot's or Flight Commander's Address	17. Color of Aircraft
FLYING X RANCH – BOX 3 CORNUDO, N.M.	BLACK/WHITE

*If IFR flight, give elapsed time until arrival over point of first intended landing.
If VFR or DVFR flight, give elapsed time until arrival at destination.

SEE REVERSE SIDE

CLOSE FLIGHT PLAN UPON ARRIVAL

Form ACA–398 (7–58)

marked in bold, blue ink. Randy looked at the back of the chart and saw that their symbols were different. By merely glancing at the chart, a pilot could tell whether an airport was civil or military, or used jointly by the two; he could also tell whether it had service facilities, or only provided a landing area. Small figures gave the elevation above sea level, the length of the longest runway, and told whether the runway was hard-surfaced· and lighted.

Randy found a list of airports on the back of each chart that gave more detailed information about fueling and repair facilities, and restrictions to the use of the airstrips. He was interested to note that the Flying X airstrip was described as "Private. Stock on field."

37

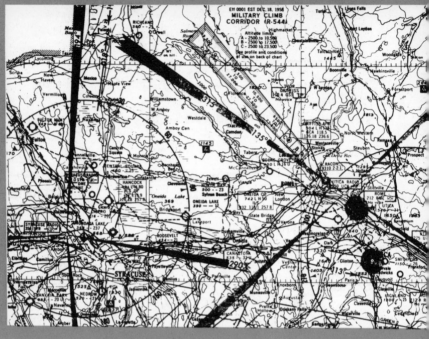

Sam was examining the Los Angeles sectional chart. "Boy! Look at all of these restricted areas where airplanes can't fly!"

Randy looked at the back of Sam's chart. "Sure! Here's a listing of them. Here's the Point Mugu and Vandenburg missile ranges—who'd want to be conked by a falling nose cone?—and a whole bunch of artillery ranges and gunnery and bombing practice areas. You can sure see why they keep you out of places like that. And I see this one place here, called California Restricted Area Complex, where they're testing ultra high-speed aircraft. We could fly there, but we'd have to stay under 20,000 feet."

AERONAUTICAL SYMBOLS
AERODROMES

AERODROMES WITH FACILITIES

LAND	WATER	
⬡	⬡	Civil
⬡	⬡	Joint civil and military
⬡	⬡	Military

| ✕ | Principal civil aerodromes in large populated areas; or air terminals of major importance |

AERODROMES WITH EMERGENCY OR NO FACILITIES

LAND	WATER	
O		Landing area
	⚓	Sheltered anchorage

AERODROME DATA

LAND

HARMON
18 L H 46
Airport of entry
GCA ILS DF
278 119.9 126.18
257.8 122.7G

18	Elevation in feet
L	Minimum lighting
H	Hard surfaced runway
46	Length of longest runway in hundreds of feet

WATER

oo	Elevation in feet
L	Minimum lighting
S	Normally sheltered take-off area
62	Length of longest runway in hundreds of feet

NAS ANACOSTIA
oo L S 62
2870

VHF OMNI-DIRECTIONAL RADIO RANGE (VOR)

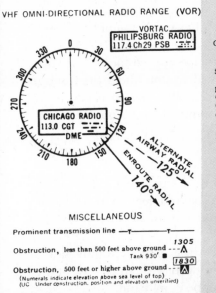

VORTAC
PHILIPSBURG RADIO
117.4 Ch 29 PSB ▪▪▪

CHICAGO RADIO
113.0 CGT
DME

ALTERNATE AIRWAY RADIAL — 125°
ENROUTE RADIAL 140°

MISCELLANEOUS

Prominent transmission line ──T────T──

Obstruction, less than 500 feet above ground ──△ 1305
Tank 930' ▪

Obstruction, 500 feet or higher above ground ──△ 1830
(Numerals indicate elevation above sea level of top)
(UC Under construction, position and elevation unverified)

TOPOGRAPHICAL SYMBOLS

Contours	Reliable	1000
	Approximate	
	Depression	
Swamps & Marshes		
Landmarks (with appropriate note) (Numerals indicate elevation above sea level of top)		▪ Factory ▪ Stack 875'
Oil Tanks		▲ ▲
Oil Fields		
Dams		
Rapids and Falls		
Elevations (In feet)	Highest on chart (devoid of tint)	•1115
	Highest in a general area	•1085
	Spot	•950
Mines and Quarries		⚒
Mountain Passes		)(
Lookout Stations (Elevation is base of tower)		⊛ 75(Site) 1025(Elev)
Ranger Stations		↟
Coast Guard Stations		• CG 79
Pipe Lines		PIPE LINE
Race Tracks or Stadiums		RT
Open-Air Theaters		▽ Open-air Theater

Sam thought a minute. "I wonder if that's where they test the X-15?"

"Could be," said his brother. "But with the X-15 going up over 100 miles, I don't think we have to worry about it hitting us in the Cessna."

"Here's your uncle, boys," said Mrs. Morrow, "I think we're about ready to go."

"Flight plan all filed, weather seems to be ideal. We may run into some clouds in New Mexico, but we'll check again when we land for fuel and lunch at Winslow, Arizona."

"Will we be grounded if we hit heavy weather, Uncle Glar?" Randy asked.

"No, son, this plane is equipped with an omni-range radio. I'll explain it once we're airborne. Now excuse me while I do a quick line check."

The rancher made a careful examination of the Cessna, checking the propeller, wheels, control surfaces, and other external parts of the airplane. He opened the engine cowling and checked the oil, fiddled around under the fuselage for a moment as he drained a little gas to check it for water and impurities, then climbed up to open the caps and inspect the contents of the wing fuel tanks.

"Gee, Uncle Glar, don't you trust the fuel gauges?" Sam said.

"I'd rather find out about a stuck fuel gauge on the ground, than a couple of thousand feet in the air with an empty gas tank. The only way to be sure you've got gas, is to *look*."

The rancher switched on the engine. Randy saw at once that the Cessna was equipped with an electric starter and did not have to be "propped" by hand.

"We have to check the instruments to be sure all of the plane's engine parts are operating satisfactorily. Then we have to wait until she's warmed up. If this was a jet, we could take right off. But it's very dangerous to take off in a cold piston-engine ship."

Uncle Glarfie advanced the throttle and showed the boys how this made the engine turn faster. They watched the indicator on the tachometer, an instrument that gave the number of engine revolutions per minute.

When the plane was warmed up, the rancher contacted the tower on the two-way radio and received his takeoff instructions. Then they taxied out on the proper taxi strip and headed for the end of their runway. As they moved along, Randy was horrified to see his uncle take his hands from the wheel and take a pair of sunglasses from a case in his pocket.

"Hang on, Uncle Glar!"

"Don't worry, Randy. When a plane moves on the ground, you steer it with your *feet*. You use the rudder to steer in your own propwash."

"Cessna three-one-one-seven-nine cleared for takeoff," said the control tower radio.

Uncle Glarfie spoke into his microphone, "Three-one-one-seven-nine, Roger."

Randy saw him advance the throttle to its widest. The engine roared, and the plane moved down the runway—and within what seemed like a very short run, the Cessna had lifted.

"So long, L.A.," Sam called. He looked out of the cabin window. "Boy, look at the traffic jam on the Freeway!"

"We didn't see much of the ground features when we were flying in the 707," Randy remarked. "I think it'd be pretty tough to navigate when you fly so high and fast."

"Jets fly mostly by omni-range," Uncle Glarfie said.

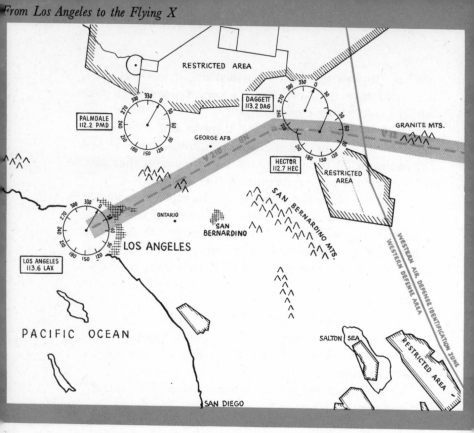

"They use special charts with a lot of radio navigational information printed on them, and not much other detail.

"But, Uncle Glarfie!" Sam protested. "You said that *this* plane navigated by ommy—ommy—"

"Omni. It's from a Latin word that means 'all.' It refers to the way that omni stations transmit their signals in all directions. Omni works for light planes and commercial jobs, as well as for military jets."

The boys' uncle explained that in former days, aircraft radio navigation was done by means of low-frequency stations. The signals they generated were often drowned

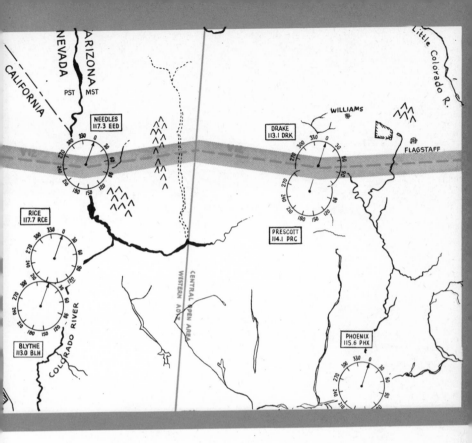

out by static. Furthermore, the beam was sometimes bent or shifted, causing the pilot to stray off course. The system was also tricky to use—especially if you were not too well experienced with it.

The omni-range system used very high frequencies that were not subject to heavy static, bending, or shifting. Uncle Glarfie said that the omni stations could be thought of as radio guideposts. The country was sprinkled with them.

"Can you show us how to use the omni?" Randy asked.

"It's not too difficult. First, take a look at that chart.

43

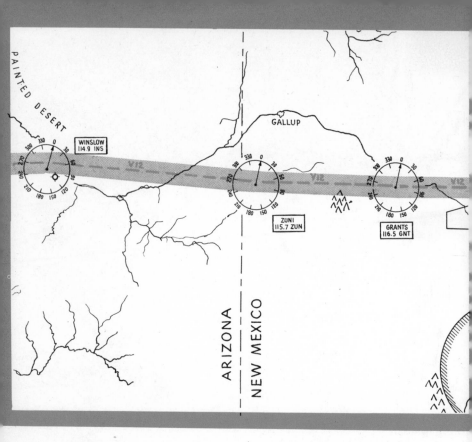

See the compass roses printed in dark blue? Each one of those marks the position of an omni transmitter. There'll be a little box somewhere inside the rose with the name of the station, its frequency in megacycles, and the identifying code signal it transmits."

"I see one," said Sam. "It says, *Palmdale Radio—112.2—PMD.* Then there are a bunch of dots and dashes."

"Morse code for PMD. The station broadcasts in Morse. Now! Because the frequency is so high, our receiver can only pick up the transmission when we're within line-of-sight of the transmitter. Do you understand what that means?"

44

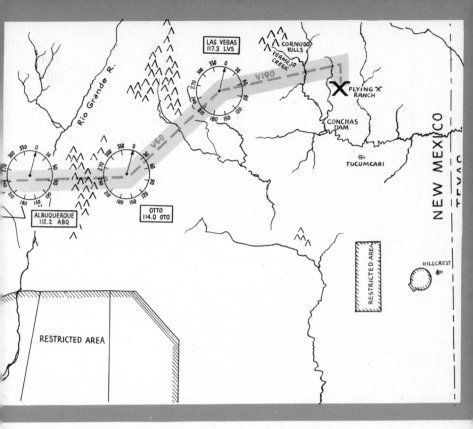

"Sure, Uncle Glar," Randy said. "If the station is below the horizon, we don't receive it. It's the same with TV and FM signals."

"Of course, the range of reception varies with the altitude of your aircraft. The higher you are, the better. If the country's flat, you have a range of about 50 miles at 1,000 feet. At 5.000 feet, the range is over 100 miles. At 10,000, the range is 150 miles. A jet that climbs to 50,000 feet can receive an omni station for 320 miles."

Uncle Glarfie said that there were several ways to use the omni. The simplest involved following straight-line courses that passed over one omni station after another.

"We'll use the omni to fly to the ranch. It will save searching for landmarks, and your old uncle is a mighty lazy flyer!"

Randy was poring over the chart. "What course are we flying now?"

"We're going from Los Angeles toward Daggett omni. If you line up the two, you see that we should have a bearing of 42 degrees."

"On course!" Sam said, looking at the compass.

"A coincidence, if you're going to be honest about it. We aren't flying by the compass—we're flying by *this*." The cattleman pointed out a small VHF receiver. "This is the omni receiver. I'll turn it up so that you can hear the station. It's Los Angeles, and it's transmitting LAX. We don't have to listen to the code, except to identify the omni, so I'll turn down the volume."

Uncle Glarfie showed the boys a selector knob on the receiver that was turned until a meter was centered on 42 degrees. An indicator in the center of the meter read FROM, because they were moving away from Los Angeles.

"See the needle on the meter? That's what we steer by. All we have to do to keep on course, is make sure that the needle stays centered. If it drifts right, we steer right until we're back on course. If it drifts left, we steer left. The beauty of the omni system is that it automatically compensates for wind drift. If the needle is centered, you know you're on course."

"No sweat!" exclaimed Randy. "Now I see why it's a lazy man's way to fly!"

"After a while, when Los Angeles fades out, we turn the selector to 222 degrees—that's 42 plus 180, because we use the reciprocal bearing now—and tune in the Daggett omni. By looking at the chart, we see that it has a frequency of 113.2 and a code of DAG. When we start reading the station, the indicator in the center of the meter reads TO."

Randy said, "And we just keep flying to Daggett?"

"No—we're going to change course here, at the Barstow radio beacon, and we'll have a bearing of 260 toward the Hector omni. We keep chugging on and eventually pass directly over Hector. The omni needle jumps around for a few moments, and the code signal gets blurry. Then the indicator snaps over to FROM, and the needle steadies again."

"I see," said Randy. "And you can keep going from omni to omni that way."

"Even though the ceiling is zero," his uncle said. "If you look on the chart, you'll see that Los Angeles and Daggett are connected by a blue line that has the compass bearing printed right on it. The line also has some other numerals on it."

"I see them—V 210 and V 8 N."

"Those identify this civil airway, just as Route 66 identifies a certain highway. We're flying on Victor 210 and Victor 8 North. The Victor airways are the highways of the skies."

"Do you *have* to use them?"

"No, but it's convenient—especially on long cross-country trips. On our flight plan, we've designated that we'll fly Victor 210 to Barstow checkpoint, then Victor 12 to Winslow, where we'll set down for fuel and lunch. We follow 12 all the way to the Otto omni in New Mex. Then we take Victor 60 to Las Vegas, then Victor 190 to the edge of the mesa. From there, we pilot into the ranch airstrip by eyeball instrumentation."

Randy had been following this flight plan on the three

charts. "Suppose the visibility is poor when we get off the Victor airway? How can we find the ranch?"

"Sometimes it's tough," his uncle laughed. "Seriously, if it was really bad, I'd have to set down at the Las Vegas, New Mexico, airport by means of omni approach. Then —" he shrugged "—we wait for the weather to go away."

"I guess .omni takes care of getting lost, doesn't it?" Randy asked.

"Some pilots could get lost on the end of a string! But omni is really a wonderful help, even if you're not flying the Victor airways. If you're within range of two omnis, you can get cross-bearings and pinpoint your position."

He explained how this could be done. First, the aircraft would gain all the altitude it could, to get maximum range. Then the pilot would select a likely station, tune it in, and turn the course selector until the needle was centered.

"Suppose he got a 180-degree FROM bearing. Okay. Draw a line on the chart to correspond. Then pick up a second station, center the course selector again, and draw a second line. The place where the lines intersect is the ship's position."

As the plane flew along, Randy practiced tuning in several of the other omnis within range and got bearings from them. When he laid out these bearings on the chart, he found he could pinpoint the Cessna's exact position along Victor 210.

"This is really great," he said admiringly.

"You'll be able to learn a lot more about aerial navigation from Carlos and his pals," said the rancher. "They hope you'll be joining them at their Civil Air Patrol meetings."

"Civil Air Patrol—?" Randy looked happily confused.

Sam giggled. "And Randy was moaning low about being stuck all summer with nothing to navigate but a horse!"

Randy turned red, but his uncle only laughed good-naturedly. "Even us cowpokes have taken to the air now."

"Empty saddles in the old corral," Sam sang. "We're riding the omni-range tonight!"

CIVIL AIR PATROL
USAF AUXILIARY
CORNUDO
SQUADRON

AIR-AGE CADETS

THE CESSNA CIRCLED the Cornudo airport, and Uncle Glarfie radioed for permission to land. They had reached New Mexico by late afternoon.

"I thought we weren't going to land at the airport," Sam said.

"You and your mother and I are going on to the ranch," Uncle Glarfie said. "But I'm dropping Randy off at the airport. There's a Civil Air Patrol meeting this afternoon, and Carlos and Dana are there." The rancher turned to Randy. "I think you'll enjoy meeting the boys there instead of waiting until they return to the ranch."

"Sounds swell, Uncle Glar," Randy said.

Sam pulled a long face. "How come *I* can't go?"

"CAP cadets have to be 14, Sam. You're still a little

shy, I'm afraid. Tell you what, though — we'll find out whether you can attend a meeting as a special guest some time."

The Cessna was descending toward the asphalt runway. In a moment or so it touched down.

"A perfect three-point landing!" Sam said.

"Not really," his uncle smiled. He began to taxi the plane toward a small building at the far end of the field. "You see, some planes have a two-wheel landing gear and a tail wheel. These are the *real* three points. Other planes, like jets and this Cessna, have a tricycle landing gear. The third wheel is the nose wheel."

The rancher explained that landing an aircraft of the first type necessitated stalling the plane — getting rid of its lift — at the precise moment of touch-down. If this was done, the plane would land "three-point" — on its two wheels and its tail. However, if the plane landed when the wings still had some lift, it would bounce back up into the air again. On the other hand, if the pilot stalled the plane when it was still a few feet off the ground, the aircraft would thud down jarringly.

"So you see, in order to make a perfect three-point landing, a pilot needs experience and good judgment. But a tricycle gear makes it much less tricky. You can land too fast on the tricycle gear and still stay on the ground. You don't really have to stall the plane to land it. In fact, some guys have compared tricycle landings to just driving down out of the sky!"

The Cessna came to a stop in front of a concrete-block building, painted blazing yellow, that had a sign above the door. Randy read it:

CIVIL AIR PATROL
USAF AUXILIARY
CORNUDO SQUADRON

Uncle Glarfie opened the door and hopped out of the plane. Randy alighted on the opposite side, and accompanied his uncle into the building.

The place was full of boys and girls. Some wore uniforms of cotton khaki; some wore levis; one girl had on a brilliant red squaw dress.

Several of the young people called out, "Hiya, Mr. Haines!"

"Where's Major Bullock, Nita?" the rancher asked the girl in the squaw dress.

"Helping Dana get his lecture set up, Mr. Haines. Dana's going to tell the guys about life in the Air Force Academy. Us gals are going to listen in so we'll know how to cope with the cadets on football weekends!"

The cattleman laughed. "Nita, I'd like you to meet my nephew, Randy Morrow. He's come for a vacation at the Flying X, and I suggested that he might be interested in the CAP. Randy, I'd like to introduce Nita Welles."

"Hi," said Randy.

"We'd like to have you sit in on our meeting, Randy," the girl said. "Do you know anything about the CAP?"

"I've read about your search and rescue missions," Randy said tentatively.

"That's just one part of CAP activity. We have an aviation education program, and a radio net, and —"

"Yo, Dad!" called a loud voice. A tall youth in a CAP uniform separated from the swarm. His eyes flicked over Randy in cool appraisal, then he grinned. "I'll bet I know who *you* are, amigo. You're my cousin Randy from Tenderfeetville. Welcome to woolly New Mex! Needless to say, I am Cadet Captain Don Carlos Haines y Montoya —"

Nita made a choking noise and started to laugh. "Better known as the Ego-Eagle!"

Carlos scowled. "Silence in the ranks! Especially the *female* ranks!" He took Randy by the arm. "Just come along with me, amigo. I'll brief you on the setup and introduce you to the rest of the Las Conchas unit of the squadron."

Uncle Glarfie said, "I'll have to get out to the ranch. Carlos, be sure that you and Dana and Randy get home in time for supper. Tia Maria is cooking up a special meal for tonight."

"R-r-roj!" said Carlos, smacking his lips.

When the big rancher had gone, Carlos and Nita led Randy over to a group of three boys who were engaged in a heated argument over a diagram on a blackboard.

Nita whispered, "They've been working on the rockets and missiles section of the CAP education course."

A blond, deeply tanned boy was drawing a rocket trajectory on the board. "I say the second stage rocket fires *here* — when the first stage is as high as it can get."

"You're nuts, Dunlap — it fires *here,* right after the first stage's fuel is all used up!" A dark boy with a keen, pointed face grabbed the chalk and marked a big X on the board.

"I think both of you guys are all wet," said the third boy, the possessor of a weird crew-cut that stuck up in short spikes all over the top of his head.

"Be of good cheer! Don Carlos is here!" Randy's cousin announced breezily.

"Now we're really snafu-rooney," grumped the spike-haired one.

"Come, come, men —" Carlos peered at the diagram. "What seems to be the beef?"

"Give us a fix on this rocket firing sequence," said the boy with the dark, Latin face.

"Well — um — " Carlos frowned importantly, then

53

Three boys were engaged in a heated argument.

scratched his head. "Why don't you dig up the Willy Ley book and look it up?"

"Lobo borrowed it and left it home," said the blond boy.

Randy said, "We had a big argument about step rockets in the club I belong to back in Chicago. We call ourselves the Solar Missileers Amateur Rocket Society."

The three boys at the blackboard looked at Randy with a "who's he?" expression. Carlos proclaimed grandly, "Allow me to present my long-lost cousin and our new-found companero, Randy Morrow. Randy, these guys are Wash Dunlap, Lobo Verdugo, and Cactus Jack McKenzie. Now! You say you are a rocket expert?"

"Heck, no! But I do remember the argument we had about step rockets. Our club moderater — he's an old artillery man — finally straightened it out."

Taking the chalk, Randy explained that since acceleration was what was needed to enable a rocket to rise against gravity, the second stage should fire when the first stage was going fastest, not when it was highest.*

"At the high point in the trajectory," Randy went on, "the rocket has slowed down almost to nothing. Fire the second stage there, and you get only the acceleration of the second-stage engine. But if you fire it when the first stage is going fastest, you can add the stage-one g's to the stage-two g's." Randy looked hopefully at the CAP cadets. "Got the message?"

Cactus Jack smiled speculatively at Randy, and ran his hand over his head, re-arranging the spikes. "Y'know, Randy-Dandy, I think we can *use* you!"

"Yeah," said Lobo, still staring at the diagram. "Aviation used to be nice and simple. But since they got on this spaceman kick — "

*See *There's Adventure in Rockets,* by Julian May, p. 92.

"How about you guys helping me find out more about airplanes," Randy suggested, "and maybe I can give you a leg up on the rockets."

Carlos clapped Randy on the back. "Amigo, we read you loud and clear!"

"Attention!" An adult voice rang out from the far end of the room. The cadets snapped-to alertly. A man in uniform whom Randy guessed must be the CAP commander, Major Bullock, stepped up onto a rickety little lecture platform. Standing at his side was a young man. The blue shoulder boards and distinctive cap identified him as an Air Force Academy cadet. So this was Cousin Dana!

"As you were," Major Bullock said. Almost all of you know Dana Haines, a former member of our squadron who entered the Air Force Academy last year. We invited Dana to tell us a little about life in the Academy. He accepted — with the provision that his talk be strictly informal. So I'd like to suggest that you all make your selves comfortable."

There was a shuffling and scraping of chairs. Randy and the others of the Las Conchas unit sat perched on the edge of the workbench.

Then Dana began to talk, and Randy could not help but admire his easy manner. There was something that made his older cousin stand out — an air of being ready to assume responsibility and carry out a job successfully. Dana Haines looked like a man who would become an excellent leader. Randy felt proud to be his cousin.

"I know a lot of you CAP cadets want to enter the Air Force," Dana said. "There are many ways to do it, of course. I think that the Air Force Academy way is the best — but then, I'm a little prejudiced."

The boys and girls laughed.

56

"The mission of the Academy is to produce good Air Force officers. What do you get when you graduate? Well, from the general education program, you get a bachelor of science degree. The military airmanship program gives you a rating of Second Lieutenant, and an aeronautical rating of navigator.

"Those are only part of what you get from the Academy. The cadet's training gives him a sense of honor, duty and discipline. It prepares him for leadership and teamwork, and shows him the role played by airpower in our national defense.

"That's the mission. Now you'd probably like to know how the mission is accomplished. Well, during the first year, the cadet is a Fourth Classman. He arrives at the Academy in early summer, and begins what amounts to basic training. He learns military courtesy, discipline, drill, and procedures. He becomes familiar with basic weapons and learns how to prepare aircraft for missions. By the time Fall Term begins in September, the new Fourth Classman really feels that he's a member of the cadet wing."

Dana described a cadet's day, which began at 6:00 A.M. Before classes, the cadet had breakfast and prepared his half of the two-man room for inspection. Then it was time to scoop up his books and proceed to classes "on the double."

"The courses are heavy in science and mathematics. You take such things as chemistry, algebra, plane trig, analytical geometry, and calculus. During the Fourth Class year, you take U.S. history, cartography, and world geography — in addition to English department courses. In the last three years, you specialize according to your aptitudes. But you must take physics and political science during the Third Class; mechanics, thermodynamics, electrical engineering, economics, and psychology during the Second Class; and astronautics, aerodynamics, philosophy, law, and a foreign language during the First Class. Of course, you're taking flight training and physical ed throughout all four years."

Dana paused for a moment. He could see that several of the boys were anxious to ask some questions. "I think this is enough lecture," he said. "Suppose you ask me the things you'd like to know. Let's start with Cactus Jack."

"Dana, does a guy have to be a science whiz to get into the Academy?"

"No, but it goes without saying that anybody who wants to enter will be well versed in aeronautics. You should also know your math, and have a good background in high school science subjects. You'll have to pass the entrance exams to be accepted, and the questions deal with science, math, mechanics, aviation, and English composition."

Another boy spoke up. "How about the physical exam? Can you tell us what kind of things disqualify a guy?"

Dana explained that the physical standards for Air Force pilot training were generally used to select the candidates. A young man would have to have 20/20 vision without glasses, and no other eye defects. He would have to be not less than 5 feet 4 inches tall and not more than 6 feet 6, with weight in proportion to height.

Common medical defects that would disqualify a candidate included imperfect vision, perforated eardrums, hayfever, heart trouble, hernia, severe acne, emotional instability, and uncorrected dental defects.

"If a candidate is exceptionally well-qualified in an academic sense, he might be admitted with a medical waiver for certain minor physical defects. Cadets with a medical waiver don't enter pilot training when they graduate, however."

"Do you have to be a big brain to get into the Academy?" asked a very young cadet.

Dana smiled. "If you did, you could scrub *me* right from the start! No — you have to be qualified to enter college, and you have to maintain a 70 average in your studies once you're accepted."

Other boys asked how to apply for entrance to the Academy, and Dana referred them to the literature that was available in the CAP library. "There are so many ways to be nominated that I've forgotten some of them. But you can get the dope from your CAP commander, Major Bullock. Actually, your Civil Air Patrol training is the best possible preparation for a guy interested in entering the Academy and becoming a jet pilot."

"There speaks the loyal alumnus," Major Bullock commented with a smile.

Dana spoke about many of the other facets of cadet life. Of the flight and navigation training, of the altitude chamber indoctrination before the first flight in a jet, of his thrill at taking the jet's controls for the first time.

"It must be terrific," Randy whispered to Nita, who sat beside him on the workbench.

"You don't have to be an Academy cadet to take a flight in a military jet," she whispered. "CAP cadets can do it, too!"

Randy looked at her in blank astonishment.

"Ask me after Dana is finished."

Major Bullock addressed the group. "I think I speak for all of us when I thank Dana Haines for telling us about the Air Force Academy. We all want to wish you good luck with your studies there, Dana. And we hope you'll be getting some company from Cornudo squadron before too long."

The boys and girls cheered and clapped. Many of them rushed up toward the platform to question Dana further. But Randy turned to Nita and asked anxiously, "Did you mean what you said about CAP cadets getting to ride in jets?"

"Our cadet training program has a series of achievement steps. After you've completed six of them, you become eligible for the jet orientation course, which includes some basic instruction in flying a jet."

"Holy mackerel," said Randy.

"Only outstanding CAP cadets are chosen," Nita warned. "You'd have to work pretty hard, Randy."

"I never knew there *was* such a thing available to teen-age guys!" Suddenly his face was clouded. "But, Nita — I don't know how to fly. I could never join the CAP."

"Cadets don't have to be pilots, silly," she laughed. Most of the members of this squadron have student certificates — but all that means is that we're in the process of learning to fly. We scrounge whatever flight time we can with the Cornudo instructors, working toward the 40 hours we need to obtain our private pilot license." Nita looked somewhat rueful. "But CAP can't foot the bill for our lessons. We have to earn money for them ourselves— and sometimes it's tough! We cadets are lucky if we can log a few hours of flight time a month."

Rand said, "I see. But a private pilot's license is sure something worth shooting for!"

Nita nodded. "I really envy you, Randy."

"Why — what do you mean?"

"Staying at the Flying X. With the Haines family."

"I still don't get it."

"You mean that you don't know that Mr. Haines used to be an Air Force flight instructor?"

Randy just stared at her. She said, "If you went about it right, you could probably learn to fly this summer."

Across the room, Carlos called, "Hey, Randy! C'mon over and meet my brother! Randy? *Randy!*"

"Snap out of it, boy," Nita whispered. "The summer is just beginning!"

CHAPTER FOUR

WESTERN-STYLE WINGS

THE JEEP BOUNCED over the rutty range road that led to the Flying X ranch. Dana drove, while Randy, Carlos, Lobo Verdugo, and Cactus Jack McKenzie hung on to various pieces of hardware and tried to keep from being tossed out.

"Hey, Dana! Throttle back!" Carlos protested.

His big brother laughed. "I keep trying to get this thing off the ground!" He slowed down an imperceptible trifle. "So Randy's all set to join the CAP, eh?"

"I've got the application for Mom to sign," Randy said. "What I plan to do is to join here in New Mexico, then transfer to a squadron near home when I go back to Chicago in the fall."

The jeep swung off onto a side road labeled V-BAR

RANCH. They roared up to the ranch buildings and dropped off Cactus Jack and Lobo.

"See you guys tomorrow," Carlos said. "Bring plenty of Jetex pellets."

"Roj," said Lobo.

The jeep jack-rabbited away. "What's — a Jetex — pellet?" asked Randy, between jolts.

"Fuel for model jet engines," Carlos explained. "You'll be building several plane models to qualify for your CAP achievement steps. How about starting with a jet? I'd be glad to let you build one of the kits we have out at the ranch."

"Gee, Carlos, can't I just stop at a store and buy a model? I hate to scrounge one of yours."

"Amigo, the nearest hobby shop is 40 miles away, back in Cornudo. So stop insulting our Western hospitality. You can start building the kit as soon as you like. After supper, maybe."

"Supper!" Dana stomped down on the accelerator again. "I heard Tia Maria talking about roast kid for supper!"

"Any kid we know?" Carlos cackled. "I'll bet ole Randy-Dandy here never tasted roast kid. Aiyeee!" Carlos rolled his eyeballs up into his head and assumed an expression that presumably represented rapture.

"That's a new one," Randy admitted. The jeep hurtled toward the crest of a rise, then topped it. "Hey — is that the Flying X?"

In the valley below flowed a small river with the buildings of a large ranch west of it. To the east, on the other side of the river, Randy saw an airstrip.

"That's the spread," Carlos said. "Gun these wheels, will you, bird-boy?"

The jeep, trailing a great cloud of dust, rolled into

the ranch. The boys hurried to the tree-shaded patio, where Mrs. Morrow and Sam sat with Uncle Glarfie and a slender, striking woman with a knot of black hair at the nape of her neck.

"I'm your Aunt Dolores," she said warmly, taking Randy by the hand. "I hope these two desperados haven't teased you too much!"

"Carlos and Dana have been swell," Randy said. "I really enjoyed the CAP meeting."

"All set to join, Randy?" asked his uncle.

"Why — how did you know?"

"Call me psychic," the rancher said smugly. "Before the summer is over, you'll be well on your way to being a full-fledged junior birdman."

Randy took a deep breath. "Uncle Glarfie, will you teach me how to fly?"

"Why, Randy!" exclaimed Mrs. Morrow. But Uncle Glarfie silenced her with a polite gesture.

"I will," he told Randy, "if you're willing to work hard at it, and if you're seriously interested in aviation."

"How can I prove that I'm serious?"

"Well, you can begin by studying for your CAP primary training."

Carlos said, "Randy's going to build a flying model, Dad. How's that for a starter?"

"That'll do just fine. Randy — you build a flyable model. Show me that you understand what keeps a plane in the air. Do that, and I'll work out some flight instruction for you."

"Uncle Glar," Randy said, "you've got yourself a deal!"

Supper was over, and Randy, Sam, and Carlos had taken over the long, polished wood table of the ranch-

64

"I'm your Aunt Dolores."

house dining room. Carlos had brought out several of his own completed models, and was showing them to the Morrows.

"Before you start to build the model," Carlos said, "you have to learn the parts of an airplane. The *fuselage* is the plane's body. All of the other components of the aircraft are attached to it. It also serves to carry the pilot and payload."

Carlos told the Morrows that there were two main types of fuselage construction. Truss-type construction, used mostly in light planes, consisted of lengths of steel tubing, the *longerons,* interconnected by other tubes, the *struts.* Lighter-weight elements, the *stringers* and *formers,* were added to the truss structure to streamline the fuselage. Covering of fabric or thin aluminum, the *skin,* was used to enclose the framework.

"The skin of a truss-type fuselage doesn't bear any flight force. It just serves to keep the wind out."

Carlos showed the Morrows a model that was constructed according to the truss principle. The framework was of lightweight balsa wood, and the skin was tissue paper.

"Now look at this model jet. It's something like the one you'll be making. It's made of balsa entirely, and it represents the second type of fuselage construction — hollow or monococque."

"Mono-*what?*" Sam asked.

"Mono-*cock.* In this type, the skin bears the flight forces. The model is a pure monocoque because it has no interior bracing at all. The balsa skin is strong enough for a model. But most full-scale jets are *semi-monocoque* construction. They have some interior bracing, but most of the load is borne by the skin."

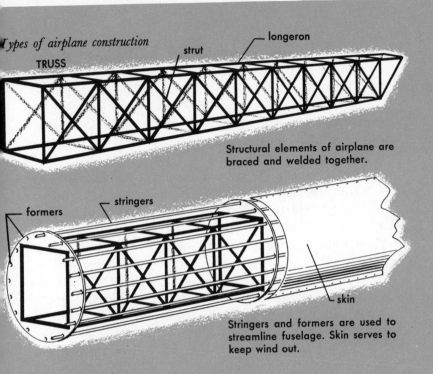

TRUSS

strut

longeron

Structural elements of airplane are braced and welded together.

formers

stringers

skin

Stringers and formers are used to streamline fuselage. Skin serves to keep wind out.

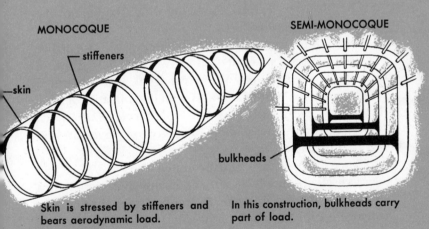

MONOCOQUE

stiffeners

skin

Skin is stressed by stiffeners and bears aerodynamic load.

SEMI-MONOCOQUE

bulkheads

In this construction, bulkheads carry part of load.

67

"What advantages do the two types have?" Randy asked.

"Truss-type is very simple. It's used when the fuselage doesn't have to carry very many passengers or a large jet engine. Hollow-type construction is used in ships that carry lots of passengers and cargo, and in jets with their bulky engines."

Randy asked, "What're these flight forces that you keep mentioning?"

Carlos explained that there were many forces that acted on the fuselage. The propeller on a piston-engined plane imposed torque, which tended to twist the fuselage around. As the wings rose and lowered, other twisting forces were applied. Up-and-down motion of the tail imposed a different type of force. The attachment of wings, landing gear, and other components imposed still other stresses.

"An aircraft designer has to take all of these forces into consideration," Carlos said.

The Morrows learned about the wing, the part of the airplane that supplied lift.

"We'll talk about what lift is later, when we figure out what makes a plane fly. For now, we'll just think of the wing as a component of the plane. It can be mounted in several ways. Our Cessna is a high-wing monoplane. The model jet is a mid-wing monoplane. The Beech Bonanza is a low-wing monoplane. Monoplane means that the aircraft has a single wing.

"I see two wings!" Sam protested.

"Everybody speaks of a plane having two wings. But technically there's only one, extending right through the fuselage. Biplanes have two wings located one above the other. There used to be a triplane with three wings, and I once saw a picture of ship with even more wings than that. It looked like a flying venetian blind!"

Using a sheet of paper, Carlos sketched wing shapes. He also pointed out that the front of the wing was called the leading edge, while the rear was known as the trailing edge. The place where the wing panels joined the fuselage was the wing root. The bracing members on high-wing planes such as the Haines family's Cessna were called struts.

"There are three types of wing structure. In cantilever wings, all the bracing is inside the wing. In semi-cantilever construction, the wing is partially braced inside, and the rest of the stress is taken up by a single strut on each side. Externally braced wings have several struts that carry all of the load.

"The wing tips are usually set higher than the wing roots. The angle is called positive dihedral. There's negative dihedral, too, but the only modern planes I can think of that have it are the P6M-1 and the F-104."

Carlos explained the control surfaces of the wing. *Ailerons* were hinged sections that were found on the trailing edge, more or less near the wing tip. They were connected so that when one aileron went up, the other went down. They were used to roll the plane to one side or the other.

"*Flaps* look something like ailerons, but they're closer to the wing root, and are connected so that they both go up or down at the same time. They can increase or decrease the wing's lift."

"What good does that do?" Sam asked.

"Increased lift helps in a quick takeoff. Decreased lift

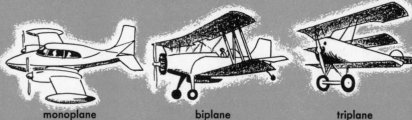

monoplane   biplane   triplane

Monoplanes are capable of fast flight. The biplane is still used for crop-spraying and other jobs where low-speed flight is desired.

high-wing   mid-wing   low-wing

Monoplanes are classed by the manner in which the wing is mounted on the fuselage.

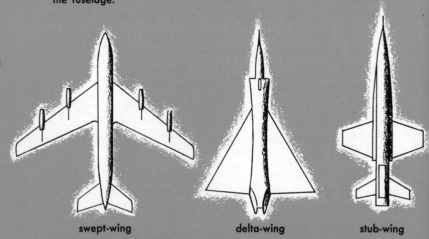

swept-wing   delta-wing   stub-wing

High-speed flight demands special wing shapes. These designs help airplanes penetrate sonic barrier smoothly.

helps in a quick landing. Some planes also have trim tabs on the trailing edge, used for adjusting the plane's balance under changing load conditions."

Then Carlos explained the tail assembly, or *empennage*. The *fin*, or vertical stabilizer, stuck straight up. It tended to keep the plane from swinging from side to side. Its after section was the hinged *rudder*, which could be moved to the right or left.

"Lots of aviation beginners think that the rudder makes the airplane turn, just like the boat rudder makes the boat turn. *This is wrong*. The rudder just makes the tail swing left or right, a movement called yawing."

There were some airplanes that had more than one vertical stabilizer. Another type, the V-tail or butterfly-tail design, had no vertical stabilizer.

The horizontal stabilizers were also part of the tail. They formed a small wing, at the trailing edge of which were the elevators, hinged sections that moved up or down together.

"You mean that the elevators make the plane go up or down?" Randy asked.

"Wrong, amigo! The elevators don't elevate! They don't cause the plane to gain or lose altitude. They simply raise or lower the tail. This is a very difficult thing for the beginner to catch on to, for some reason. You'll find out more about it when you learn to fly."

When he learned to fly! Randy's heart gave a bound. Carlos has said *when*, not *if*. . . .

"You're not listening, amigo," Carlos chided him.

"What — ? Gee, I'm sorry, Carlos. Go on."

"As I was saying, V-tail planes have the two stabilizers attached to the tail at an angle. The V arrangement combines horizontal and vertical stabilizers and their control surfaces. Some fast jets don't have the horizontal stabilizer and the elevator hinged. They're a single unit attached to the plane by a pivot so that the whole thing can be tilted up or down."

The elevators also had trim tabs on them. Carlos explained that there was a trim adjustor in the plane's cockpit that enabled the pilot to make certain adjustments of elevators and ailerons in order to compensate for light or heavy cargo, different flight speeds, emptying fuel tanks, or conditions of landing or takeoff. If the pilot had his trim adjusted properly, his plane should fly level without his touching the controls at all.

"Now," Carlos said, "I trust you have all the terminology set. I will now deprive you of the joy of my presence. I've got studying of my own to do. Screech if you need help with the models."

Randy and Sam set to work, using the tools that Carlos had helped them assemble. They had pocket knives, razor blades in holders, sandpaper, pliers, scissors, and cement.

There were two types of models under construction. Sam's was a truss-type, made of balsa and tissue paper toughened with airplane dope, and powered with a rubber band. Randy was building a hollow, all-balsa model of a jet that would be powered by a Jetex engine.

Several hours later, the boys' parents and their aunt and uncle came in to inspect the model-builders' progress.

"We won't finish the job tonight," Randy sighed.

"It takes time to make a good model," Uncle Glarfie said. "You have to give the joints time to dry and grow strong."

"You've done very well, though," Aunt Dolores said. "But now I think it's time to head for the bunkhouse. You've got a lot of riding to do tomorrow."

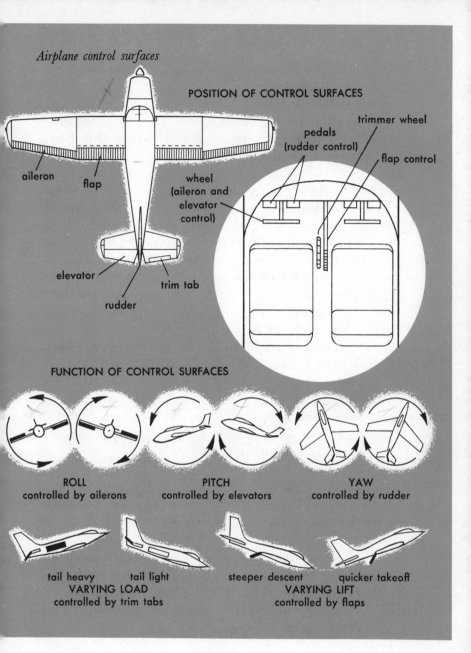

Airplane control surfaces

POSITION OF CONTROL SURFACES

aileron

flap

wheel
(aileron and
elevator
control)

elevator

rudder

trim tab

pedals
(rudder control)

trimmer wheel

flap control

FUNCTION OF CONTROL SURFACES

ROLL
controlled by ailerons

PITCH
controlled by elevators

YAW
controlled by rudder

tail heavy   tail light
VARYING LOAD
controlled by trim tabs

steeper descent   quicker takeoff
VARYING LIFT
controlled by flaps

73

"Riding?" Randy looked surprised. "Carlos said we'd be flying models tomorrow."

Uncle Glarfie smiled. "You'll be doing it Western style, way out on the range. None of your round-in-a-circle, city backyard type of model flying! Out here, we've got wide open spaces!"

It was slightly after dawn the next morning when Carlos tumbled them out of their bunks. They dressed and ate breakfast while they were still half asleep, then helped Carlos collect the flying models he planned to test.

"We'll take the good old bentwing," Carlos said detaching a model F-86 from its hook on the wall of his room in the bunkhouse. "Randy, you carry this new delta job. And Sam can take this big band-driven plane and have a ball while we fly the jets."

The sound of hoofbeats floated in through the open window, and a couple of coyote howls sounded.

"There's Lobo and Cactus Jack," Carlos said. He leaned out of the bunkhouse window and howled in brief acknowledgment, then turned to the Morrows. "They're waiting for us. The wrangler will have our ponies ready at the corral. You guys all set?"

"Roj!" said Sam.

The sturdy Western ponies trotted over the open range toward a saucer-shaped depression several miles from the river.

"That's our flight-test area," Carlos said, reining his mount close to Randy's. "We'll stash our stuff under the trees by that draw. That'll be our base of operations."

"Not much wind today," Cactus Jack called out. "This should be a good day for stability tests."

The ponies trotted over the open range.

"Yeah," Lobo added. "Nobody'll be able to use the wind as an excuse for sloppy plane performance."

The boys dismounted and hobbled their ponies, then began to prepare their miniature craft for flight. Sam wound up his plane's rubber band and launched it. The rest of the boys paused to watch the plane climb. It angled up very steeply, seemed to "hang on the edge" for a moment, then tumbled down out of control.

"Stalling," Cactus Jack remarked. "What kind of nose weight d'you have in her, Carlos?"

Sam picked up the fallen plane and brought it over to his cousin. Carlos inserted a probing finger into the front of the little plane, then said, "Part of the weight's gone. We used a hunk of 'dobe, and it crumbled."

"Gosh," Sam said. "Won't the plane fly without the weight?"

"Nope," Carlos said. "She'll keep stalling because her center of gravity is off. Can't get the right kind of lift with the center of gravity shifted."

"Lift?" Sam asked.

"Roj. The force that makes the airplane fly." Carlos stooped down and picked up several small pebbles from the ground. "Any of you guys have any gum?" he asked.

Lobo dug a battered stick out of his levis. Carlos presented this to Sam with instructions to chew it until the sugar was gone. "We'll use it to make a new weight."

Randy said, "Lift is the force that counteracts gravity, isn't it?"

"Roj. Lift and gravity are two forces that act on a plane in flight. The other two are thrust and drag. Do you know what makes a plane stay up in the air?"

"Uh — the flow of air over the the wing?" Randy guessed.

What makes an airplane fly?

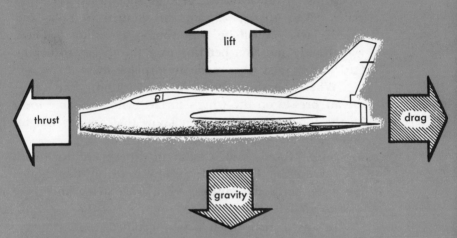

Four forces are acting upon an airplane in level flight: thrust, furnished by the engine; lift, furnished by the wing; drag, the resistance offered by the aircraft to the air; and gravity, which pulls the airplane toward the earth.

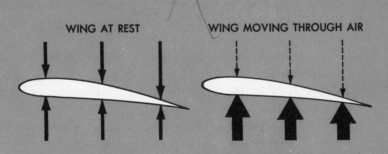

WING AT REST

WING MOVING THROUGH AIR

When an aircraft is at rest, atmospheric pressure (arrows) is equal above and below wing.

In flight, forward motion of wing produces low-pressure area above wing. High pressure below holds wing up.

77

Carlos sat down on the ground and picked up Sam's plane. "You guys go ahead," he shouted to Lobo and Cactus Jack. "We'll be with you in a minute." Then, with Randy and Sam bending over the model with him, Carlos explained what made an airplane fly.

"When the ship stands on the ground — like this — the air presses on the wing's surface with the same force on the top and bottom. You know that air has weight, don't you?"

"Sure," Randy said. "I did an experiment once with a big syrup can. Put a little bit of water in it, then boiled the water until the can was filled with steam and there was no air left in it."

"It was a real stitch," Sam grinned reminiscently. "Randy screwed the top on the can and took it off the fire, then we cooled the can off by tossing a little water on it. Powie!"

Carlos said, "I'll bet the can looked like a sledge hammer hit it. When the steam condensed into water, it left a vacuum in the can. Air pressing on the outside of the can crushed it. Actually, air pressure at sea level has a force of about a ton per square foot."

"Wow!" exclaimed Sam. "How come we aren't squashed?"

"Because the pressure is the same inside and outside our bodies," Randy said.

"Let's get back to the resting wing," Carlos said sternly. "Right now, air is pressing with equal force on the upper and under sides." Then he picked up the model and moved it slowly through the air. "But when the wing moves, something happens. Notice how the upper surface of the wing is more curved than the lower surface? That's called the camber.

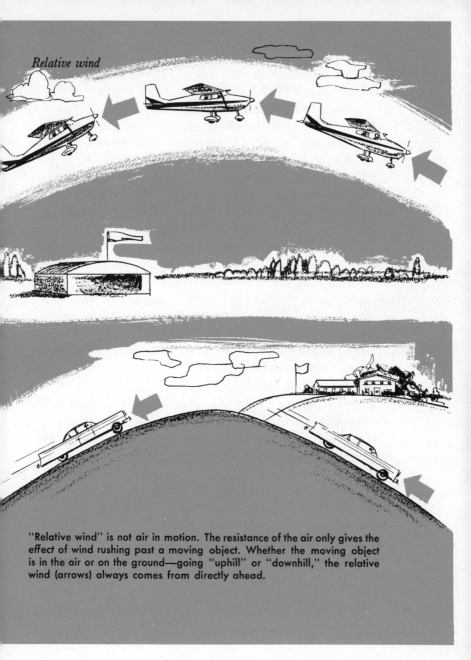

Relative wind

"Relative wind" is not air in motion. The resistance of the air only gives the effect of wind rushing past a moving object. Whether the moving object is in the air or on the ground—going "uphill" or "downhill," the relative wind (arrows) always comes from directly ahead.

"As the wing moves forward, imagine a couple of air molecules right at the leading edge. One of 'em is going to travel over the top, and the other one is going to travel under the bottom of the wing. *Both* of 'em are going to arrive at the trailing edge at the same time! Now — which one do you suppose will have to move faster?"

"The one going over the top," Randy said promptly. "It has farther to go, so it'll have to move faster to arrive at the trailing edge at the same time as the low-road molecule."

"Roj. And for reasons we don't have to go into, *fast-moving air* exerts less atmospheric pressure than slow-moving air. So when air moves over this wing, we get less pressure on the top than there is on the bottom. The air molecules above are pushing down — and the result is lift."

"Does the air always have to be moving before there's lift?" Sam asked.

"There always has to be a *relative* wind," Carlos said. "Relative wind is a phrase that you often hear airmen use. It's the wind that you feel when you poke your hand out of a fast-moving car, even though the air outside may register dead calm on a wind gauge. You feel the wind because the car is moving through the air. It's the same with flying. The plane's power plant makes it move forward through the air, and a relative wind is created. Only the airplane experiences the wind's full force. That's why it's called relative."

"I think I get it," Randy said. "But what about a stall? That's when the lift force suddenly goes blooey, isn't it?"

"Well, it doesn't really happen suddenly, unless the

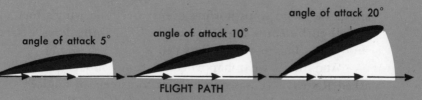

Angle of attack is angle between flight path and wing. When aircraft flies at high angle of attack, pilots say ship "mushes."

The angle of attack is always based upon the flight path, not the ground. Notice how the angle of attack can remain constant even though the angle with reference to the ground is changed.

plane is caught in a gusty wind." Carlos rubbed his chin thoughtfully. "Let's see — do you know what's meant by angle of attack?"

The Morrows shook their heads.

"You have to understand that to understand what causes a stall. Angle of attack is the angle the wing presents to the relative wind. The leading edge is higher than the trailing edge. It's got to be that way if the plane is to fly. Now at any given air speed, the angle of attack determines the amount of lift that the wing'll develop. Small angle, small lift. Large angle, large lift — *up to a point.*"

Randy said, "You mean there's a maximum angle of attack?"

"Roj! For most wings, it's about 20 degrees. At this

angle, the wind stops flowing evenly over the wing's top. It gets turbulent — starts to burble. The wing loses lift and falls. This is what pilots call a stall."

"And that's what happened to Sam's model plane?" asked Randy. "It was climbing at too steep an angle?"

"No — no — You've got to understand that the angle of attack has nothing to do with the angle the plane's wing makes with the *ground,*" Carlos said emphatically. "What matters is the angle presented to the relative wind. Let me try to explain it another way."

Carlos used the model to demonstrate. First he made the plane "fly" level.

"You might think there was no angle of attack. But there is. It's built right into the plane, and you can see it if you look at the way the wing is joined to the fuselage. First thing to remember is that the plane will stall in level flight if its airspeed falls below a certain value. Then, the relative wind just doesn't supply enough lift."

Carlos made the plane move forward on a level course, but as it moved, he pulled the nose up more and more.

"Now I'm increasing the angle of attack. Notice that the plane is still flying level. It's just the nose that's going up. Now this is an angle of about 20 degrees. Pull the nose up any higher, and the plane will stall."

Then Carlos made the model move upward and downward, meanwhile keeping the plane's nose just slightly above the flight path. He explained that a plane could climb or glide and still keep an angle of attack of a constant value.

"A plane can stall in level flight, in climbing, or in gliding — provided the nose is pulled up far enough. Sam's plane is tail-heavy. Its nose is high. It had enough power to send it along a little way before the tail dropped and the angle of attack reached a stall. But once the stall angle was reached, the plane fell."

"The gum is ready," Sam said. He and Carlos experimented with several of the stones until the right weight was found for the model's nose.

"This one looks good," Carlos said. "Prop 'er up!"

Sam wound the band on the propeller and launched his ship. It climbed gently, banking as it went, then glided down to a landing about 30 yards away. Sam ran to retrieve it.

"He's buttoned up," Carlos said. "Now let's us get going on the jets." They went over to join Lobo and Cactus Jack, who were tinkering with their models.

"Everything okay?" Carlos asked.

Jack ruffled his hair disgustedly. "Still trying to get the elevons on this delta set right."

Randy and Carlos examined the dart-shaped model jet. It had no elevators because it had no empennage, as such. Instead, the trailing edge of the delta had control surfaces, called elevons, that combined the function of ailerons and elevators.

Randy watched, fascinated, as Jack demonstrated the differences between his plane and one of the more conventional models. Ailerons, Randy knew, caused the plane to bank left or right. To bank right, the right aileron was raised and the left one lowered. The lowered left aileron increased the angle of attack of the left wing, giving it more lift than the right wing with its *raised* aileron. The different amount of lift on left and right wings caused the plane to bank right.

Elevators were really the plane's angle of attack control. With elevators raised, the nose was lowered. Lowering the elevators raised the nose.

"But with these elevons, you have to combine the two," Jack said. "I want the nose up and a certain very small angle of bank. So I've got to lower the elevons. But one has to be slightly lower than the other one to get the bank!" He shook his head. "I've used up six Jetex pellets trying to find the correct setting."

"Keep up the good fight," Carlos urged, ignoring Jack's resulting grimace. "And how are *you* doing, Lobo?"

The dark-haired boy was scraping out a small aluminum cartridge with his pocket knife. "Just getting the gook out of this engine. This model of mine is pretty hot." He tapped the little casing against his knife blade to dislodge the last scraps of burnt material. "There. All set to go again."

"Randy said, "Mind if I take a look at that?"

"Be my guest," Lobo grinned.

Randy examined the Jetex engine. It was, he saw, a tiny reaction engine, operating on the principle of recoil that propelled rockets. Two pellets of solid fuel were placed inside the casing. Then a coil of special wick was placed on top of the upper pellet, and the nozzle assembly with its washer was firmly seated on the case. A spring clip held the nozzle assembly on the case.

"To fire the engine, you take another short length of wick and poke it through the nozzle so that the inside end touches the fuel pellet. Then put the engine into its mounting clips on the model."

Lobo mounted the little propulsion unit so that the nozzle faced the tail. Randy noticed that the model's fuselage was protected with aluminum foil near the place where the jet exhaust would stream out.

"Now we're ready to light the wick." He struck a match and applied it. There was a hissing sound as the

An engine for model jets

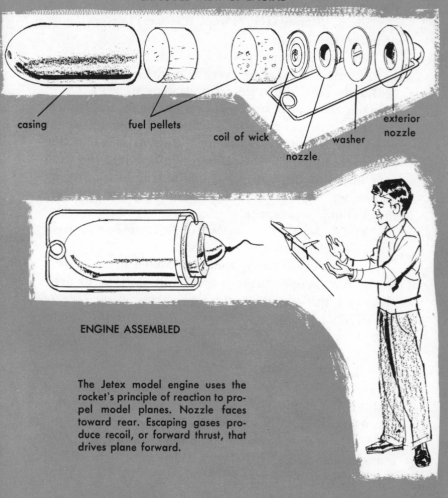

EXPLODED VIEW OF ENGINE

casing

fuel pellets

coil of wick

nozzle

washer

exterior nozzle

ENGINE ASSEMBLED

The Jetex model engine uses the rocket's principle of reaction to propel model planes. Nozzle faces toward rear. Escaping gases produce recoil, or forward thrust, that drives plane forward.

85

fuel pellet ignited. "Let her build up thrust a few seconds
—then—"

Lobo released the model. It soared beautifully into
the air. "She's got about 15 seconds of fuel."

"Sharp," Randy said. "I hope the one I'm working on
turns out half as good."

"You can get some practice by flying the bentwing,"
Carlos suggested, handing over the model F-86.

Randy took the little jet and went to work on it,
changing the control surfaces to vary its flight, and launching it at various angles to see how it behaved. A light
wind rose, and he experimented with its effect on the
plane. He found that launching the plane into the wind
gave increased lift, with the opposite true for downwind
launchings. A cross-wind launch sent the plane tumbling
into a clump of mesquite.

"You're learning," Carlos laughed, as Randy went
down into the draw after the model.

I *am* learning, Randy thought. Model planes were a
lot of fun, besides being a good introduction to aerodynamics. But something else was lurking in the back of
his mind—the words of his uncle: *Build a flyable model
and show me that you understand what keeps a plane in
the air. Do that, and I'll work out some flight instruction
for you.*

He snaked his arm through the spiny mesquite and
grabbed the silvery little jet. Down here in the draw, it
was warm and very quiet. Randy held the plane thoughtfully. Inside the plastic canopy bubble was a tiny pilot—
a model man to fly a model jet. What must it be like to
fly a real jet plane?

At that moment, Randy determined that somehow he
would find out.

86

BEYOND SOUND

July in New Mexico is a time of thunderstorms. As the hot afternoons came to a close, Randy was accustomed to take his Civil Air Patrol booklets to the porch of the deserted bunkhouse. He could study in peace there, and watch the towering thunderheads build up over the long mesa north of the ranch.

The clouds would form into great billowing cells topped with anvil heads. Thunder would begin to echo across the valley, and then a cold wind would herald the approach of a brief, violent storm. Uncle Glarfie had told him that thunderstorms, with their terrific updrafts and downdrafts, were extremely dangerous to light planes.

87

The Flying X craft was usually grounded during storm time each day.

And yet—Randy looked up from his reading. He was certain that he heard the sound of a plane's engine mingled with the almost continuous roll of thunder.

The boy searched the darkening sky. Whoever was in that plane would be in for a rough time before too long.

Suddenly the bunkhouse phone rang. Randy went inside to answer it.

"That you, Randy?"

"Right, Uncle Glar. What's up?"

"There's a plane circling our landing strip. I'd like you to go out there and meet it when it lands. Could be they're out of fuel, or maybe they just want to squat until the storm passes. At any rate, look 'em over and let me know."

"I'll get out there right away."

Randy grabbed up a slicker from a wall peg and hurried outside. One of the ranch pickup trucks stood nearby, and the boy slid into it and started the engine. As he rolled toward the airstrip, which lay about a half mile away on the other side of the river, Randy caught a glimpse of the circling plane. It was a blue and white Beech Bonanza with gaudy day-glo paint on the wingtips, cowling, and tail surfaces.

This is going to be a tough landing, Randy thought. The wind sock on the ranch hangar indicated a very strong gusty cross-wind, and even the truck seemed to shake in the blast of the approaching storm.

The Beech came in fast, with its power on. Just before its wheels touched, the ship banked shallowly into the wind. This trick resulted in the pilot's retaining perfect control, despite the dangerous wind gusts. The plane

"Help block the wheels, son!"

landed and taxied toward the edge of the earth runway.

Rain came sluicing down as the plane stopped. Randy gunned the truck over. Whoever was in the plane, he was one hot pilot!

"Hi! Your plane in trouble?" Randy yelled. There were two men in the cabin of the Beech, dimly visible through the downpour. The one on the right opened the cabin window.

"Dad!" Randy shouted in amazement.

"Help block the wheels, son. We're going to have to tie her down right here."

Mr. Morrow climbed out of the plane, followed by the second occupant, an Air Force captain. The men carried strong web straps, which they hooked to the plane's wings and tail. Randy helped fill anchor sacks with heavy rocks and attach them to the straps.

"She'll be okay now," the captain said. "Let's grab those wheels of yours, boy, and get out of here!"

The three of them ran for the truck. "That was quite a landing," Randy said, as they headed for the ranchhouse.

"Captain Holly is quite a pilot," Mr. Morrow said. "He's a flight test officer at Edwards. We're going to have to bribe him with a little varmint shooting in return for my free ride in his personal plane."

"I'll expect a mountain lion at the least," said the pilot.

But hunting was the last thing Randy wanted to discuss with the Air Force man. "You mean you're a *test pilot?* You really get to ride in all the new jets?"

"Taking rides isn't Captain Holly's job," Mr. Morrow said dryly.

"Aw, gee, Dad—I know that. But—"

The pilot came to Randy's rescue. "A test pilot's job *is* pretty exciting, Randy, but it involves a lot more than just seeing whether a new ship can maneuver without the wings falling off!"

"What *do* you do, Captain Holly?"

"Let me try to give you the whole picture, Randy. We'll start with a brand new experimental airplane. Before the Air Force ever gets the plane, it has been tested by the contractor. If the ship looks good, a flight test program for it is set up."

Captain Holly told Randy that from the very beginning of a test proposal, a flight test engineer and a flight test officer worked together as a team to evaluate the experimental aircraft. The engineer tested the ship on the ground, and the officer tested the ship in the air.

"There are three categories of testing. Category One involves testing the sub-systems of the aircraft. The engineers test such things as the control system, the fuel system, and so on. Then they make sure that everything goes together! The plane is flight-tested by the contractor and by us to see whether it's airworthy. Any minor difficulties will be corrected during the Category One phase, and the results of our testing will be incorporated in the redesigned craft. If the plane looks acceptable, the contractor will be given the go-ahead to build more ships for the Category Two tests."

"What happens if the experimental plane doesn't prove out?"

"Well, that happened with the F-107, you may remember. The plane was not accepted, but it proved to be a valuable stepping stone toward design modifications of *other* planes. The 107 went to the National Aeronautics and Space Administration for study."

If a plane passed the Category One tests, the contractor was authorized to build 10 to 20 more planes for the Category Two phase. Some of these were flight tested by the officers for performance and stability. The Pilot's Handbooks for the particular aircraft were written, using the data gathered by the experimental flight test officers. Several of the ships were sent to Eglin Air Force Base for climatic tests. Others underwent a functional development program where they received a simulated two years of flying time in six months. Still others were given instrument procedures tests at Wright Air Development Center.

"By the time a ship has been this far through the mill, we can be pretty sure that it's ultimately acceptable. Goofs do show up, but they're usually things that can be fixed. In this stage, we want to know how *practical* the aircraft is. We already know that it will fly, but we want to know if the average pilot will be able to fly it. We also want to know if the average mechanic will be able to fix it if it breaks down. Our national defense setup has no place for prima donna airplanes!"

The first 75 hours of Category Two flight testing were flown only by the Edwards flight test officers. Then the new ships were flown by the men who would actually be using them.

The Category Three phase simulated actual combat conditions. These tests were carried on at various Air Force Bases by the squadrons themselves. At the end of about 1200 hours, the plane was considered operational. All of the experimental flight test officers and ground support people were out of the picture.

Mr. Morrow grinned wickedly. "And by then, the plane is obsolete!"

"What—?" Randy was taken aback.

"This is literally true," Captain Holly said. "Usually, the original test planes go back to be retro-fitted with the modifications that have been worked out through test experience. Of course, the planes in production have changes incorporated in their design just as soon as we determine that a change is needed."

"How long does it take to get from Category One through Category Three?" asked Randy.

"About two and a half years," the test pilot said. "And a military plane can expect to have an operational life of five to six years after that."

"What kind of planes have you been flying, Captain Holly?"

"I've been working with delta-wing interceptors."

"Supersonic stuff?"

The captain smiled. "You're expecting maybe a 20-mule team?"

Mr. Morrow said, "Randy, I know you'd like to keep pumping Lee all day—but we've been sitting in this truck in front of the ranchhouse for ten minutes now!"

Randy gave a guilty start as he peered through the rain. "And there's Uncle Glar on the porch. I forgot to phone him from the airstrip to tell him it was *you* in the Beech!"

"We'll go appeal to his Western hospitality," Mr. Morrow said.

"I'll have to put the truck back, but I'll see you soon, Dad!" Randy paused, then added purposively, "And I'll see you, too, Captain Holly! I've got a lot of questions to ask you!"

It was still raining after supper, so the male members of the Haines and Morrow families took Captain Holly into the ranch trophy room, where a big fire had been kindled. It was cheerful there, with the light from the flames flickering on the pelts of bobcats and upon model planes that hung by invisible wires from the beamed ceiling. Dana had a guitar, and they sat around singing cowboy songs. Then they started in on flying songs. Uncle Glarfie contributed one from his World War II experience:

> By the ring around his eyeball
> You can tell a bombardier;
> And you can tell a bomber pilot
> By the spread across his rear.
> You can tell a navigator
> By his sextants, maps and such;
> You can tell a fighter pilot —
> But you can't tell him *much!*

Captain Holly had one that he said dated from Korea:

> Bless 'em all! Bless 'em all!
> Bless tiptanks and tailpipes and all!
> Bless old man Lockheed for building this jet,
> But I know a guy who is cussing him yet.
> 'Cause he tried to go over the wall
> With tiptanks and tailpipe and all.
> The needles all crossed and the wings both fell off,
> With tiptanks and tailpipes and all.
>
> Through the wall! Through the wall!
> The bloody invisible wall.
> That transsonic journey is sure one to cuss,
> As bad as a ride on the local base bus.
> So I'm staying away from that wall,
> Subsonic for me and that's all!
> If you're hot you might make it,
> But you'll probably break it —
> Your back or your neck, not the wall.

"I don't get it," Sam said puzzledly.

"The song refers to the sonic barrier," Captain Holly

It was cheerful in the trophy room.

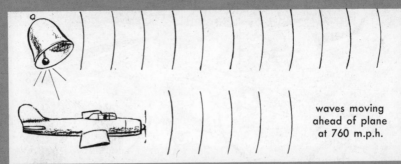

waves moving
ahead of plane
at 760 m.p.h.

plane moving at
400 m.p.h.

Sound is waves in the air. It moves at 760 m.p.h. at sea level. If a plane moves slower than this, it can push air *ahead* of it in waves.

said. "The early jets were in for a hard time when they approached the speed of sound, but sometimes it happened when the plane dived."

"It must be quite an experience to go through the sonic barrier," Randy said. "But I suppose you do it all the time."

"I do," the pilot conceded, "but you're going to be disappointed when I tell you that the barrier isn't a barrier any more. As a matter of fact, you can fly past the sonic barrier in a ship like the F-102 and *not even notice it,* unless you happen to be looking at your machmeter. It hangs up at Mach .97, then flicks on again at 1.2 when you're through the barrier. Sometimes the nose has a tendency to tuck under as the ship goes through, but that's all."

96

When an airplane of conventional design approaches the speed of sound, the air cannot flow away from it smoothly enough to sustain flight. The ship is buffeted to pieces. Specially designed, supersonic airplanes can penetrate sonic barrier.

"But isn't it like a different world on the other side?"

"Not in the ships that are designed for supersonic flight. I think this bit about suddenly entering a new world must be a holdover from the early days, when ships would vibrate and just about shake to pieces as they entered the transsonic zone, then simmer down as they passed the speed of sound."

"But," Sam protested, "isn't it *quiet* when you're flying faster than sound?"

Mr. Morrow said, "I wonder if you really understand just what the sonic barrier is?"

"Well—" Sam began dubiously. "Maybe not, really."

"Perhaps I can explain it. Then Captain Holly can tell you about the problems of flying ships faster than sound."

97

Sound, Mr. Morrow said, was nothing but pressure waves in the air. The waves spread out in all directions from whatever object was making the noise. Sound waves moved at a speed that was related to the density of the air. At sea level, the speed of sound was about 761 miles per hour. At 20,000 feet, it was only 710 miles per hour. At 35,000 feet it was 662 miles per hour, a value that stayed constant up to an altitude of 20 miles.

"Sound is a compression wave in the air. But there are other types of compression waves, too, that travel at what we call the 'speed of sound.' The type of wave that we're interested in is the one made by an airplane as it moves forward."

Mr. Morrow said that all aircraft—even silent gliders—created compression waves as they pushed the air aside. Air tended to "pile up" in front of the leading edge of the wing. It was really already moving by the time the wing penetrated it.

"Think of the plane telegraphing a warning ahead of it. The air molecules get the message, and start to stream aside to make room for the airplane."

Mr. Morrow reminded them again that the compression waves moving ahead of the airplane could only move as fast as the speed of sound. What would happen if the airplane traveled so fast that the air did not have time to stream aside in advance?

"It hits the wall?" Sam asked.

"Right. And for a plane that's not designed for transsonic flight, the wall is quite a real one! Air has mass. And compressed air has a *lot* of mass. Ramming a conventional-style wing into this mass is going to take a lot of pushing."

"But a jet engine's got the push," Sam said confidently.

"It does. But you need more than a powerful engine

Design for supersonic flight

B-58

Area rule dictates "coke bottle" fuselage shape for minimum drag.

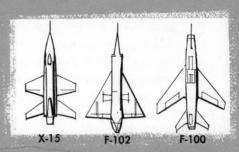

X-15   F-102   F-100

Thin wings with sharp leading edges, swept-wings, and delta wings will fly at supersonic speeds.

Skin of wing must be smooth, free from scuffs, oil patches, etc.

"Fences" on wing surface prevent air from flowing toward wingtip and destroying lift.

Special metal alloys resist heating caused by friction with air.

High speeds impose unique stresses upon airplanes. Aircraft must have special designs if they are to fly safely at supersonic speeds.

99

to get a ship safely through that wall of compressed air. Do you understand how airflow over a wing creates lift?"

"Sure," said Sam.

"Then you know that air traveling over the top of the wing moves faster than the air moving under the bottom. But now suppose that our plane is traveling at close to the speed of sound. The air flowing under the wing is still subsonic, but perhaps the faster-moving air on top is moving at supersonic speed! The supersonic air forms a shock wave—"

"What's a shock wave?" Sam asked.

"Moving air, very highly compressed, traveling faster than sound. A thunderclap is a shock wave. So is an explosion. So is the crack of a whip. But those three kinds of shock waves last only for an instant, while the ones that form on airplanes are persistent.

"Engineers have ways of taking pictures of shock waves. You can even see them with the naked eye under certain atmospheric conditions. They look like thin lines or transparent shadows. But it's their *effect* that's important. In front of the shock wave, air is traveling at supersonic speed. Right behind it, within the space of a fraction of an inch, the air is traveling at subsonic speed. On one part of the upper wing, we have low pressure from the supersonic air. On a nearby part of the wing we have high pressure when the air suddenly becomes subsonic. The wing loses lift. Sometimes the ship goes into a shock stall, or perhaps the difference in pressures will cause the wing to be ripped apart."

Captain Holly said, "And this is the heart of the whole sound barrier problem. It's relatively easy to get power enough to go through the barrier. But it's difficult to keep the plane from falling apart or going out of control during the transonic phase. Once you've passed the speed of sound, the shock waves stay attached to the wings, nose, fuselage, and so on."

The test pilot went on to say that engineers had to learn a whole new set of principles in order to design supersonic planes. It was necessary to redesign wings so that shock waves did not form at too low a speed. One way of accomplishing this was by sweeping back the wings, or by giving the ship a triangular "delta" design. Another way was to make the wing very thin and to sharpen the leading edge.

Uncle Glarfie remarked, "I hear the F-104 has leading edges sharp enough to cut you!"

"It sure does," Captain Holly said. "They keep the edge covered when the ship is on the ground so that it won't slice up the ground crew!"

"But we still haven't spoken of the thing that really makes supersonic flight a practical, everyday matter," Mr. Morrow said. "Do you boys know what's meant by the Area Rule concept of design?"

"Coke-bottle fuselage," Carlos said promptly, but Randy and Sam only looked blank.

"Well, engineers at the National Advisory Committee for Aeronautics did basic research into the flow of air around airplanes traveling at transonic and supersonic speeds. They discovered that the conventional tapered, cigar-shaped fuselage wasn't the best shape. Instead, the fuselage should be made more slender near the wing, with a curvier fore and aft section. Carlos described it pretty well as a 'Coke bottle' shape. It greatly decreases drag as the aircraft passes through the transonic zone."

Randy and Sam learned that there were many other problems connected with supersonic flight. One of the most important was high-speed heating, caused by friction

Modern Air Force jets

**Boeing KC-135
tanker transport**

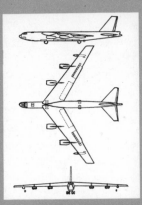

**Boeing B-52
heavy bomber-
missile platform**

**Boeing RB-47E
reconnaisance-
medium bomber**

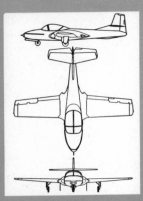

**Cessna T-37B
trainer**

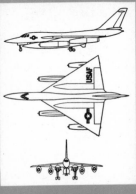

**Convair B-58
supersonic bomber**

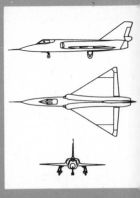

**Convair F-106A
interceptor**

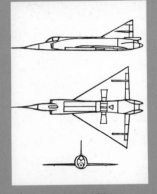

**Convair F-102A
interceptor**

**Douglas B-66B
reconnaisance-bomber**

**Lockheed F-104C
fighter**

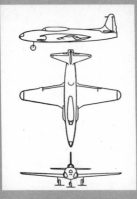

Lockheed T-33A
trainer

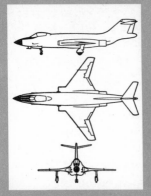

McDonnell F-101A
fighter

McDonnell F-101B
interceptor

North American F-100D
fighter-bomber

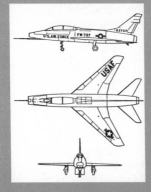

North American F-100F
two-place fighter bomber

North American T-39
trainer-transport

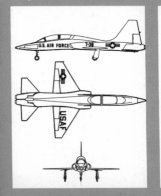

Northrop T-38
supersonic trainer

Northrop F-89H
interceptor

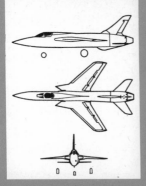

Republic F-105
supersonic bomber

with the air molecules and also by air compression at the leading edges of the airplane.

"Then there are problems connected with the new engines that are needed to sustain planes in supersonic flight. They get so hot inside that metallurgists are hard-pressed to find materials that will stand up."

Dana asked the test pilot, "Is the NASA carrying on most of the basic research in aeronautics?"

Mr. Morrow nodded. "The National Aernonautical and Space Administration is the world's greatest aero-nautical research institution. It studies problems that affect all types of aircraft—and spacecraft, too. The areas of research include basic aerodynamics, aircraft power plants, aircraft construction, and operating problems."

Mr. Morrow added that research was also going on in the labs of airplane manufacturers, in the Air Force's Wright Air Development Center labs, and in many other institutions throughout the world.

Uncle Glarfie shook his head in mock dismay. "Time was when the man flew the plane! But with all the Mach-buster refinements that these modern ships have, the pilot is relegated to being just another component — halfway between the pitot tube and the after-gafter!"

"Dad!" Dana exclaimed indignantly.

"Whatever happened to the glamor of flying?" the rancher complained, but Randy saw that there was a twinkle in his eye. "When I got my wings, all you needed was a canvas-and-wire ship, a pair of goggles, and an eagle-eyed expression on your puss."

"The look of eagles bit is still with us," Mr. Morrow smiled. "And anybody who thinks pilots have lost their glamor should take a look at the hand-painted hard hats and day-glo coveralls out at Edwards."

"The day-glo color is easy to spot if you're downed in the desert," said Captain Holly with an air of injured dignity.

"Uh-huh," Mr. Morrow grinned.

The test pilot said, "I know a supersonic-type problem that nobody's mentioned yet."

"What?" Carlos asked.

"The sonic boom!"

"There was a big flap about that in the papers not too long ago," Carlos said. "Some character claimed that the boom scared his chickens off their feed."

"I've never heard a sonic boom," Randy said. "Is it loud?"

"It's loud," Captain Holly conceded. "But most of its bad reputation comes from the fact that it's so unexpected. Nobody's surprised to hear a big crash of thunder when it's raining, but people *are* surprised when a sonic boom creeps up on them."

"I've read that the boom is even louder than thunder," Carlos said.

"It can be—under the right conditions. First, understand what a sonic boom is. It's nothing but the supersonic shock wave that's streamed off the plane."

"You mean, when the plane breaks the sound barrier, there's a boom?" Sam asked.

Captain Holly corrected him. "The boom is produced continuously, as long as the plane flies at supersonic speeds. It keeps moving along the ground, though, following the course of the airplane, so a single ground observer will only hear the sound at the instant the wave sweeps by him."

He explained that loud sounds were measured in pressure pounds per square foot. A good clap of thunder measured about one pound per square foot. The shock wave from a supersonic jet flying at 10,000 feet would have a pressure of about three pounds per square foot. Bring the plane down to 5,000 feet, and the pressure goes up to four.

"This is pretty darned loud, but still not loud enough to do any damage. The grief comes when a plane operates at supersonic speed at an altitude of about 300 feet or so. The boom pressure would jump to around 33 pounds per square foot—and that's enough to break windows!"

"But who would fly supersonic 300 feet off the ground?" Dana asked, mystified.

"Nobody in his right mind," Captain Holly said. "Actually, supersonic maneuvers are almost always carried on above 20,000 feet. At that altitude, the boom is absorbed to a great extent by the air it must pass through before reaching the ground. Randy, you probably have heard sonic booms, and not realized what they were. Most of them are barely noticeable. It's only when a ship dives that the boom is liable to be really loud."

Mr. Morrow smiled. "If Randy hasn't heard a sonic boom, he certainly will before long! It's the theme song of our jet age."

"What an age!" Randy exclaimed. Outside the ranchhouse, the echoes of a lesser thunder died away among the hills.

CHAPTER SIX

AT THE CONTROLS

Summer at the ranch seemed to Randy to move with a speed that rivaled that of the jets he had become so absorbed in. Much of the time was taken up with the affairs of the Civil Air Patrol. After attending four meetings and passing an examination on basic knowledge of aviation, Randy was accepted as a CAP cadet. The words of the cadet oath still rang in his mind:

"I pledge that I will serve faithfully in the CAP Cadets, attend meetings and activities, obey my officers, wear my uniform in a military manner, and advance my training rapidly, so that I may prepare to be of service to my community, state, and nation."

As a new cadet, Randy studied the volumes of the aviation education course, which covered such topics as navigation, electronics, aircraft power plants, aerodynamics, and the problems of air power. Together with the adult members of the CAP squadron, the cadets practiced search and rescue techniques. Randy made a special study of navigation. He had determined to win his rating as a CAP observer, flying in search planes and scanning the ground for downed aircraft.

One morning in late July, he knelt on the porch of the bunkhouse, studying an aeronautical chart. Suddenly a shadow fell over the paper, and Randy looked up to see his uncle standing there.

"You're doing very well with your CAP work, Randy."

"Why — thanks, Uncle Glar. I'm boning up on wind triangle problems. Each observer trainee is going to have to solve a 'lost plane' problem at the meeting tonight."

"Major Bullock tells me he's never seen a new cadet leap into CAP activities the way you've done. The way I look at it, you've proved that you're sincerely interested in aviation."

Randy's heart seemed to loop inside his chest. "You mean—"

"I mean that I think it's time you grabbed yourself a chunk of wild blue yonder. It's a fine morning, Randy. Want to fly with me?"

"*Do* I?" Randy scrambled to his feet. "Let's go!"

They rolled the Cessna 175 out of her hangar and gassed her up. Then Randy's uncle explained the detailed preflight inspection that was made routinely before each flight. They checked the propeller for nicks and made sure that the hub was tight. They checked the oil level

Activities of the CAP

air search and rescue

Air Force support

cadet program

disaster assistance

civil defense participation

aviation education program

communications network

public information program

109

by means of the dip stick, then drained a little gas from the tank at the bottom of the fuselage to eliminate water and impurities that had settled to the bottom.

"—And incidentally, to wash the oil off our hands," Uncle Glarfie laughed.

They checked the tires and landing gear and looked over the struts for signs of damage. The skin of each wing was examined, and they climbed up to peer into the wing tanks to make sure they were filled with gasoline. The hinges on the wing and tail control surfaces were checked to be sure that all of them were in good condition.

Then they climbed in, Randy on the left, and fastened their safety belts. "You can take over once we're airborne," Uncle Glarfie said, "but first, let's give the instrument panel a quick rundown."

The engine instruments were on the right side of the instrument panel. Uncle Glarfie pointed out such familiar ones as fuel and oil pressure gauges. There was also an oil temperature gauge, and a tachometer that measured the revolutions per minute of the engine.

"Now let's look at the flight instruments on your side of the panel, Randy. Bottom row at the far left is a clock."

"Well, that's an easy one to figure out!"

"Next to it is the barometric altimeter. It works by air pressure and has to be adjusted according to the barometric pressure of the day. See the little window on the right of the dial? You set that according to the report from the weather bureau—or in my case, according to the barometer in the hangar."

Uncle Glarfie adjusted the scale to read 29.98. He explained that the altimeter could also be set to indicate the actual altitude of the airport in feet above sea level, or it could be set to zero.

110

"In country like this, where there are mountains poking up all over the place, I keep the altimeter set for sea level. This way, when I check my aeronautical chart for obstacles, I know exactly how much clearance I have. Flying west of here, a glance at the chart shows me that I better grab a piece of sky before flying over the Sangre de Cristo Range."

"I see what you mean," Randy said, looking at the chart his uncle had pulled out. "Those mountains are over 12,000 feet high."

"For local flights around the range here, the boys sometimes set the altimeter to read zero at the airstrip's elevation, 4,800 feet. It's better to become accustomed to the sea level altimeter setting, though, and use your chart and your eyes to tell you how far away the ground is."

Next to the altimeter was the turn-and-bank indicator, a rolling ball within an oil-filled glass tube, and a needle that indicated whether the turn was left or right. Uncle Glarfie explained that the instrument showed whether a turn was being executed correctly. If it was, the ball would remain centered within two white lines on the tube. But if the ship slipped or skidded, the ball would roll to the side.

"The rate-of-climb indicator is next. It tells you how fast you're going up or down in hundreds of feet per minute. It's a valuable aid to instrument flying, but you won't have to worry about it too much now."

Above the altimeter was the airspeed indicator, one of the most important flight instruments. "It indicates the velocity of the relative wind—*not* the speed with which you're moving over the ground. Suppose your indicator shows an airspeed of 100 miles per hour—but you know that you're bucking a 30-mile head wind! Your actual

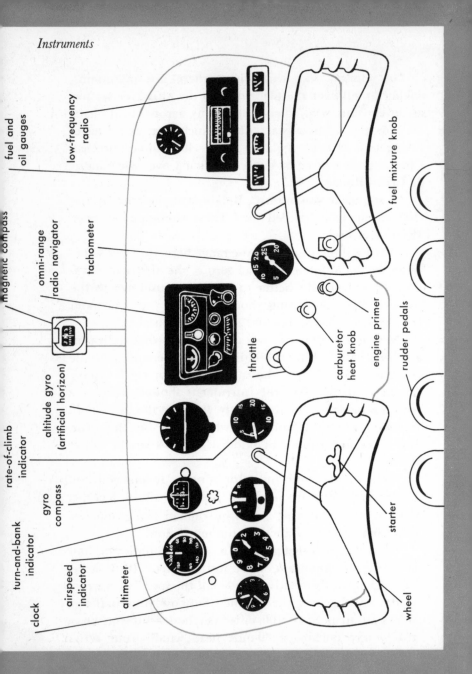

fuel and oil gauges

low-frequency radio

fuel mixture knob

magnetic compass

omni-range radio navigator

tachometer

rudder pedals

engine primer

carburetor heat knob

throttle

altitude gyro (artificial horizon)

rate-of-climb indicator

starter

gyro compass

turn-and-bank indicator

airspeed indicator

altimeter

clock

wheel

speed over the ground is only 70 miles an hour. Of course, with a 30-mile tail wind and an airspeed indication of 100, your groundspeed is 130!"

Randy thought hard for a minute. "The airspeed indicator would show when you were near a stall, wouldn't it?"

"It does—if you understand its limitations. With its power off, this airplane will stall if its speed drops to 62 miles an hour in level flight. But if the plane is heavily loaded, it will stall at a higher speed. The weight of the plane also changes when the ship is banked. During a 60 degree banked turn, this ship would stall at about 93 miles an hour!"

Randy looked a little uneasy. "But how can you tell whether a stall is coming, then?"

"You can sense it in the controls, after experience. Before that, you avoid the conditions that you *know* will make the ship stall, and you practice recovering from the stalls you'll invariably go into."

"Gee, flying isn't going to be as easy as I thought!"

"Actually, this ship is designed to help you—if you'll let it. Look out there on the left wing. See that tab on the leading edge?"

"Yes."

"That's a stall-warning indicator, the novice flyer's best friend. As long as the wing maintains the proper amount of lift, the tab stays in the *off* position. But if the wing begins to enter a stall, the tab flips because of the change in air pressure and a little horn beeps at you to warn you to get the nose down. We'll find out more about stalls later. Let's finish off the instrument panel now."

Next to the airspeed indicator was a gyro compass. It was used with the magnetic compass, which was mounted above the instrument panel. The magnetic compass was so sensitive that it swung wildly during maneuvers, and under rough air conditions. The gyro was much more stable. It was used for instrument flying, especially during landing approaches.

"We can also set a course on the top ring of the gyro and fly by keeping the bottom ring lined up with it. While we're in flight, we must check the gyro against the magnetic compass every 15 minutes or so. Gyros drift after awhile."

Next to the gyro compass was the attitude gyro or artificial horizon. A small airplane-shaped indicator was fixed in the center of the dial. A gyroscope, connected to an indicator with a horizon line marked on it, showed the position of the small airplane relative to the horizon. It indicated whether the wings were high or low or whether the plane was nose-up or nose-down.

"We're almost ready to take her up now, Randy. I'm going to demonstrate the controls for you as we go."

He did things with several of the knobs on the panel, then directed Randy to push hard with the tips of his toes against the rudder pedals. "Those are the airplane's ground brakes. Now pull the starter under your wheel."

Randy did, and the engine roared into life. Uncle Glarfie directed him to push back the starter switch and advance the throttle until the tachometer read 1000 r.p.m. When the plane had warmed up, Uncle Glarfie let Randy practice taxiing, steering the ship with pressure on the rudder pedals. It was tricky, but Randy found he could manage it with a little practice. The hardest thing to conquer was the urge to grab the wheel.

"Before we take off, we'll check the plane's two ignition systems. Aircraft engines have two spark plugs on each cylinder. We check each ignition system by watching for changes in engine r.p.m. when we switch from system to another. Ordinarily, we use both systems in flight."

When they were ready to take off, Uncle Glarfie had Randy move the Cessna down the runway and turn the nose into the wind. "On a regular airport, we'd get takeoff instructions and check carefully for other planes. Since ours is a private strip, we don't have to worry about other ships — but we *do* have to make certain there aren't any steers on the runway!"

The plane began its takeoff run. Randy watched and saw his uncle advance the throttle to full power. With only a slight back pressure on the wheel, the ship seemed to take off by itself and begin to climb.

"Be sure you understand that *lift* comes from *power*," Uncle Glarfie said. "Pulling back on the stick pulls the nose of the plane up, but power is what makes the ship gain altitude."

"What's that wheel on the floor that you were turning?" Randy asked.

"The trim control. It's adjusted for takeoff, then adjusted once more when we attain cruising altitude. Okay — suppose you tell me our present altitude."

"Um — the altimeter reads 6,000, so we must be 6,000 minus 4,800. That's 1,200 feet."

"We'll level off." Uncle Glarfie throttled back and lowered the nose of the ship. Then he invited Randy to trim the plane, explaining that if the trim was properly adjusted, the plane would maintain level flight without any effort on the pilot's part.

"Prove it for yourself," the rancher said. So Randy moved the wheel forward, causing the plane to nose down. When the boy removed his hand from the wheel, the ship leveled off by itself. Randy tried the other controls — ailerons and rudder — and found that the ship recovered by itself from their effects also. "The ship *wants* to fly right," Uncle Glarfie smiles. "Usually, it misbehaves only when the pilot forces it to!"

On his first lesson, Randy practiced straight and level flight. Uncle Glarfie told him not to watch the attitude gyro, but rather to orient himself by noticing the angle the wings made with the horizon, and noting the position of the nose in relation to the horizon.

"We've got a north wind of about 20 miles an hour. Suppose you try to fly crosswind and see what happens." Randy found that the plane began to drift. His uncle explained that this was corrected by using the rudder so that the plane's nose was headed into the wind slightly. "This is called crabbing. Notice that the ship is moving straight ahead, but the nose isn't pointed straight ahead."

"This is sure different from driving a car," the boy remarked.

"You've got three dimensions to move in instead of only two! Let's try some more turns, and you'll be even more conscious of the fact. To turn the ship correctly, you'll have to use aileron and rudder together."

Randy moved the wheel left and applied left rudder. He watched the horizon seem to tilt. When the angle had reached about 30 degrees, Uncle Glarfie told him to return the controls to neutral position. He did — and was surprised to find that the plane maintained the angle of bank all by itself.

"That was pretty good," the rancher said, "except that you've let the nose droop. To prevent this, you exert a little back pressure just as you enter the turn."

He told Randy that to come out of the turn and bank,

After checking out airplane and warming up engine, ship is taxied to takeoff runway. Note plane heads into wind.

Throttle is opened smoothly to fullest extent. When ship starts to lift, nose is raised to climb altitude.

he should apply the opposite aileron and rudder pressures. On this ship, more rudder and less aileron were needed to come out of a turn smoothly. "Just remember that to go into a turn and bank, use lots of aileron and little rudder. To come out, use lots of rudder and a little aileron."

As he practiced turning and banking, Randy felt himself gradually begin to relax. This was great! The ship didn't fight him if he treated it gently — it almost seemed to help! A sense of timelessness stole over him as he flew over the rolling range lands, circling the Flying X and the V-Bar, following the winding bed of the creek down to its confluence with the Canadian River south of the ranches.

But at last Uncle Glarfie said, "Time to head for home, Randy."

117

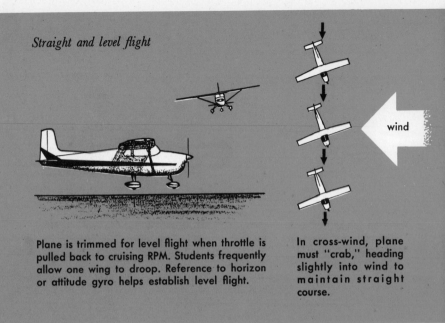

Straight and level flight

wind

Plane is trimmed for level flight when throttle is pulled back to cruising RPM. Students frequently allow one wing to droop. Reference to horizon or attitude gyro helps establish level flight.

In cross-wind, plane must "crab," heading slightly into wind to maintain straight course.

The boy sighed as he headed the Cessna northward once more. "I could sure keep this up all day, Uncle Glar."

"We'll have another lesson soon. Meanwhile, you can study some flight manuals I have back at the ranch."

"How long do you think it'll take me to solo?"

"Randy, soloing in a few hours of flight instruction isn't the mark of an expert airman. Dana and Carlos weren't permitted to solo until I felt that they understood something of what flying was all about. What you know and what you can do are the important things. You didn't learn to drive a car expertly in five or six hours, and you shouldn't expect to solo a plane in that time either — despite the things you see in the gung-ho movies and TV programs."

His uncle told him that FAA regulations required a

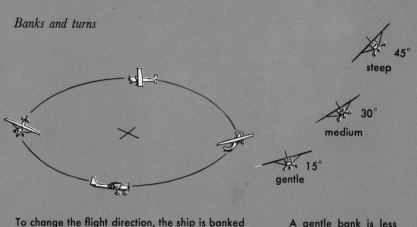

45°
steep

30°
medium

15°
gentle

To change the flight direction, the ship is banked and turned by means of coordinated pressure on rudder and ailerons. Pressure is released when bank is established.

A gentle bank is less than 25°. A medium bank is between 25° and 35°. A steep bank is from 35° to 50°.

minimum of 40 hours flight time for a private pilot's license, but only 20 of those needed to be solo hours.

"You'll solo when you're ready to, Randy. You've done very well on your first flight, you know. I seem to recall that my boys turned pretty green the first time they took the controls."

"Wait'll I get down on the ground," Randy predicted solemnly. "I'll take one step out of the plane and collapse!"

Uncle Glarfie laughed. "There's the strip. We'll make an ordinary 90-degree approach. First we scout the airstrip. See the windsock? It shows us that the wind's still out of the north. We come downwind, then turn left and fly crosswind. We can estimate the velocity of the wind by the amount of crab we need to maintain straight flight."

119

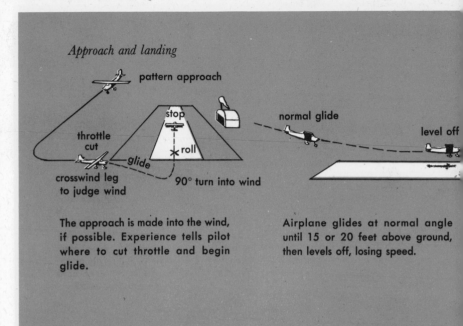

Approach and landing

pattern approach

throttle cut

crosswind leg to judge wind

glide

stop

roll

90° turn into wind

normal glide

level off

The approach is made into the wind, if possible. Experience tells pilot where to cut throttle and begin glide.

Airplane glides at normal angle until 15 or 20 feet above ground, then levels off, losing speed.

Randy saw that his uncle closed the throttle and started to glide on the crosswind leg. When he was about 200 feet above the ground, he made another left turn that brought the ship into the wind in line with the runway.

"See any steers, Randy? No? Then down we go."

The plane settled toward the earth, and Randy was suddenly conscious of how fast they were going. It would take a lot of experience, he decided to set a plane down exactly where you wanted it to land.

"The idea in landing is to keep the ship in the air just above the ground until the wings have lost most of their lift. If you land too fast, the ship is likely to bounce back into the air. This ship has a tricycle landing gear, and I think I mentioned that it doesn't have to be landed three-point style. You don't *have* to stall it just

120

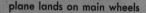

plane lands on main wheels

plane rolls to stop

Nose is raised more and more as stalling speed is approached. Airplane now only a few feet above ground.

At moment of stall, airplane should have touched down. Tricycle-gear planes can be landed before stall point is reached without bouncing.

at the point of touch-down, but you should try to have it very near the stall point before you touch. This plane should be landed on the main wheels, with very little weight on the nose wheel. When the ship touches, she'll roll along nicely on the three wheels if you put the nose down."

The ship rolled gradually to a halt. Uncle Glarfie let Randy taxi her to the hangar, and showed him how to shut off the engine by leaning the fuel mixture and turning off the ignition.

"Well, that's it, Randy! Do you have any questions about your first flying lesson?"

"Just one, Uncle Glar."

"Shoot."

"When can I have the *next* lesson?"

SPEED LIMIT
3,000 M.P.H.

THE C-47 FLEW SOUTHWARD toward the Air Force Base, and the ten CAP cadets inside peered eagerly out of the cabin windows.

"Man, look at all that white sand down there!" Cactus Jack exclaimed. "Looks just like snow in the middle of August!"

"I see the sled track ahead," Randy said. "What a long thing it is! Doesn't look like there's anything doing on it, though."

Lobo said, "Maybe they'll schedule a high-speed run during our visit."

Nita, the only female cadet in the group, said amusedly, "Of *course* they'll put on a command performance just for our benefit! What naive male conceit!"

Lobo glowered at her. Then he assumed an expression of detachment and remarked to Randy, "What a waste of time to bring dames on these visits. Everybody knows that the jet age belongs to us men."

Nita's face turned scarlet. "Is that so! Hasn't anybody clued you to the fact that there are women aeronautical engineers, and women in the Air Force?"

"But no women jet pilots!" said Lobo triumphantly. "Isn't that right, Major Bullock?"

The squadron commander thought for a moment. "I can't think of any woman who makes a career out of flying jets. But there are several who have flown them. I think that when light civilian jets get on the market, there'll be more and more women checking out in jets."

"G'wan," said Lobo scornfully. "It takes a man to handle that much airplane!"

Major Bullock shook his head. "You're wrong. A jet has more power than a piston-engine plane — that's true. But a jet *also* has hydraulically boosted controls. You don't wrestle with a jet, you speak gently to it! Since women usually have a more delicate touch than men, I wouldn't be surprised if they could get the hang of jet technique even faster than the average man."

Carlos stiffened and said. "You realize that this is treason, sir?"

The major shrugged. "You know how the gals went for power steering on automobiles? Well, jet flying is the *ultimate* in power steering."

"So watch out, junior jet jockey," Nita said smugly. "Us dolls will fly rings around you yet!"

123

A light jet airplane — the T-37

U.S. AIR FORCE

The twin-jet T-37 is a trainer airplane, used by the Air Force to give jet flight instruction to student pilots. Although it is scarcely larger than a lightplane, the T-37 has many of the handling characteristics of more powerful jets. It cruises at 332 mph at 35,000 feet.

Lobo said, *"When* the small civilian jets come out. By the time that happens, you'll be pushing grandmothersville."

Nita appealed to the squadron commander. "Is it going to take that long to develop small private jets?"

"You may be surprised to know that there's already a light jet in production that could easily be adapted for private flying. Right now, it's being used as a military trainer."

"I know!" Randy exclaimed. "The T-37!"

"It's a sweet little ship," Major Bullock said. "Just 27 feet long, with two J69 turbojet engines. Her speed max at 35,000 feet is about 390 miles an hour, and her range at a cruising speed of 310 is about 900 miles."

"And it could really be adapted for civilian use?" Nita asked wistfully.

"If there was a demand — and if the planes weren't needed for national defense. The military model carries two, seated side by side. The civilian job would probably be modified to seat four, and that would probably cut down on its range somewhat unless they used different engines."

"I wonder, though," Randy said thoughtfully. "Jets use up an awful lot of fuel. And aren't the planes pretty expensive, sir?"

The commander nodded. "Randy, you've hit on the two major obstacles to private jets. The fuel consumption is terrific, even though the engines use jet fuel, which is a lot cheaper than high-octane aviation gas. As to the high cost of the plane, that could be reduced if they went into quantity production. But the ships will probably always be much more expensive than piston jobs."

"Who would use private jets?" Cactus Jack asked. "Businessmen?"

"Probably the likeliest prospects," Major Bullock agreed. "Where an executive's time is worth big money, you get a reasonable value per mile out of a jet."

"I can see it now," said one of the boys dramatically. "The famous cattle baroness, Nita Welles, blasting off in her private jet to inspect her spread in Argentina!"

The male cadets laughed uproariously, but Nita only said, "Stick around, amigos," and winked.

The C-47 had rolled to a halt on the airstrip at Holloman Air Force Base, and the ten cadets now stood in neat ranks outside the plane. Major Bullock outlined the schedule that they would follow during their visit to the Air Force Missile Development Center.

"We're here primarily to learn about the work being done at the Center's Aeromedical Field Laboratory. But one of the doctors is also going to give us a general rundown on the problems of man in flight. As all of you well know, human beings weren't engineered to function at high altitudes. Our normal place is at the bottom of earth's ocean of air. If we're going to insist on winging into the stratosphere, we'll have to find ways to keep our bodies operating under the unfavorable conditions we'll find there. That's one of the problems. Another one involves acceleration — g-force, you hear it called. Jets move fast, and they subject the body to stresses and strains that it almost never experienced when it stayed safe on terra firma. There are other problems — but I'll leave their explanation to the experts." ·

The cadets marched to a waiting bus that drove them to the aeromedical lab buildings. They disembarked at the main one and filed to a large room where chairs had been set out for them. The room was filled with equipment, and the cadets crowded interestedly around two man-sized dummies wearing pressure suits and helmets.

"I've heard guys say these suits squeeze you pretty hard," one of the boys said. "Wonder how comfortable they are?"

"About like an all-over girdle, I'll bet," Nita said. "Isn't this silver-colored suit nice? This is the one *I* want to wear."

"Attention!" said Major Bullock. A broad-shouldered lieutenant colonel wearing dark glasses had entered the room. His hair was gray, but his face was young. The CAP commander introduced him as Dr. Valentine. "The doctor will explain the equipment you've been examining, and he'll also answer questions you might have about survival at high altitudes."

"Did you cadets notice this chart?" the doctor asked. They hadn't, but they gave it their attention now. It was a cross-section diagram of the earth's atmosphere.

"Almost everybody knows that earth's atmosphere gets thinner and thinner as you go higher. At 18,000 feet, it's only half as dense as it is at sea level. At 34,000, you've halved the pressure again. What's this going to do to the human body? Let's pretend that we're taking a ride in an altitude chamber, and find out."

At 10,000 feet, Dr. Valentine said, night vision was seriously affected. The eyes were less than 75% as efficient as they were at sea level. At 12,000, they were 50% efficient. At 15,000 feet, a pilot would be subject to fatigue, drowsiness, headache, and poor judgment. These symptoms would creep up on him more swiftly at 18,000, together with a false sense of well-being, poor muscle control, and loss of memory.

"Above 18,000, we start figuring the time of useful consciousness for unacclimatized people. You've got five minutes at 20,000, three minutes at 25,000, a minute and a half at 35,000, and about 20 seconds at 40,000. Now let's figure out what's to be done about the situation."

The doctor told the cadets how early pilots raised their ceilings by simply sucking oxygen from a cylinder through a tube held in the mouth. "This kept him in pretty good shape up to about 20,000 feet. But it wasn't very efficient. Over on this board, here, I've mounted several types of oxygen masks that raise man's ceiling even higher. The one with the little balloon is the continuous-flow mask. It's good up to 25,000 for routine use, and it'll sustain you at 35,000 for short periods if you don't move around much. The mask gives off a continuous flow of oxygen. It never stops filling the balloon. This type of oxygen system is still used in light planes.

"The mask next to it is a historical relic — a supply and demand mask used in World War II. It delivers oxygen mixed with outside air on demand, whenever you breathe in. Its regulator has an aneroid barometer in it that senses the altitude, and automatically changes the percentage of oxygen and outside air as you go up. At about 34,000 feet, you get pure oxygen. Lots of pilots swear this old A14A mask was the most comfortable ever invented."

The doctor shrugged and smiled. "But the airplanes kept going higher and higher, so the pilot had to follow. An ordinary demand oxygen system is only good up to 40,000 feet under emergency conditions. Above this, not even pure oxygen will keep you going. The atmospheric pressure just isn't sufficient to push the oxygen into your lung tissues."

The answer to this was pressure breathing. Pure oxygen, under pressure, was forced into the lungs by the

Oxygen equipment raises man's ceiling

Early aviators sucked oxygen from tube, could fly up to 20,000 feet for a few minutes.

Continuous-flow oxygen mask was developed in 1930's, is still widely used in light planes.

Demand mask furnishes oxygen when flyer breathes in, is less wasteful, raises ceiling to 35,000 feet.

Pressure-demand mask raises ceiling to 50,000 feet, forces oxygen into lungs under pressure.

Pressure helmet has been worn at 200,000 feet. It is neoprene-coated fabric balloon, seals at neck.

Modern MA-type helmet is more efficient, eliminates re-breathing of expired air.

system. The pilot had to exert effort to exhale, reversing the ordinary breathing pattern.

"The pressure-demand system is used routinely on flights in jets below 50,000 feet. Even at that, you can't take too much pressure breathing. It tires you out and slows down circulation. So what'll we do? Our long-haired pals in the physiology research department tell us to increase the pressure around the *outside* of the body. You can do this by pressurizing the cabin — but that's not going to help you if the cabin pressure fails suddenly. What we do, for safety's sake, is wear some type of pressure suit that will automatically exert pressure on the outside of the body if the cabin pressure system conks out."

The doctor invited the cadets to inspect a gray-green pressure suit, worn by one of the dummies.

"This MC-3 suit exerts mechanical pressure. It squeezes! Notice the inflatable tubes that go up the arms, down the sides of the trunk, and down the legs. They're called capstans. When they're inflated, the capstans pull on these crossing tapes and tighten the fabric of the suit around the body. These laces allow the suit to be adjusted to the body of the wearer."

The doctor removed the white helmet shell from the dummy's head so that the cadets could see the fabric helmet beneath. "This is the MA-2 high-altitude helmet. It has a neoprene-coated fabric lining that pressurizes the entire head. Over that is an inelastic nylon covering with laces for size adjustment. We'll take off the transparent facepiece so you can look at it."

The doctor pointed out that the hose was flexible, but not corrugated. It was more rugged and dependable than the rubber hoses used on earlier suits. The face-

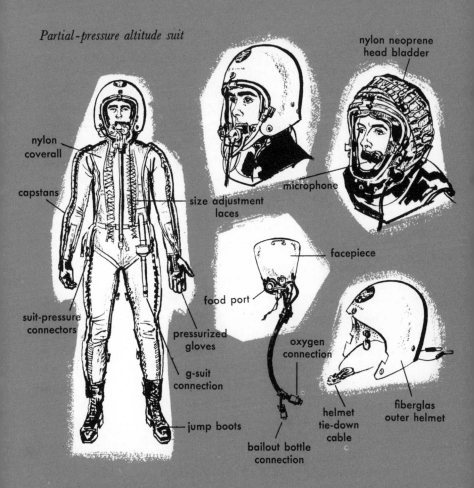

Partial-pressure altitude suit

nylon neoprene head bladder

nylon coverall

capstans

size adjustment laces

microphone

suit-pressure connectors

pressurized gloves

facepiece

food port

oxygen connection

g-suit connection

jump boots

helmet tie-down cable

fiberglas outer helmet

bailout bottle connection

This MC-4 partial-pressure suit incorporates a g-suit. Skin tight, it is worn over special underwear and tailored to fit airman. Mechanical pressurization is exerted on limbs by inflation of tubelike capstans.

Helmet is separately pressurized, seals at neck. Facepiece contains breathing valves, food port, wire defrosting grid. Helmet tends to rise when pressurized, so tie-down cable is used to anchor it.

plate had a small valvelike port, through which a tube could be inserted. This made in-flight eating and drinking possible.

"What are these little wires embedded in the plastic of the faceplate?" Randy asked. The cadets had been passing the plate 'from hand to hand, looking through it experimentally.

"Heating wires," Dr. Valentine said. "They prevent the formation of fog or frost on the plate. Now when the pilot wears the suit, he also uses accessory equipment. These are pressurized gloves. See the attachment on the back? There's a bladder built into the back of the glove, but the fingers are left free to move. Tight-fitting boots keep the feet pressurized sufficiently without any bladder action."

"Dr. Valentine?" One of the boys waved his hand. The medical man nodded. "What would happen to a guy if he went above 50,000 feet *without* a pressure suit?"

"We know he'd die from oxygen lack. But something else would happen, too. The fluid in his body would turn to vapor. The blood, for example, would come to a cold boil, swelling and distending the tissues. You'd be in hopeless shape before long. So if you want to fly high, you'd better decide to get used to the suit!"

"What about this silver suit?" asked Nita, pointing to the second dummy. "It doesn't look quite so — so confining!"

The doctor chuckled. "What you see is only the outside coverall of the Air Force MC-2 full-pressure suit. The inside garment is still classified, but I'll describe how the suit works. Incidentally, young lady, as I was coming in, I heard you say you'd prefer this style!"

All of the boys laughed, and Nita turned red. But Dr. Valentine held up a restraining hand. "Don't laugh

132

Full-pressure altitude suit

Modern full-pressure suit is relatively light in weight. Special flexible joints permit movement when suit is pressurized.

External coverall of metallized fabric reflects heat, protects airman in case of bailout or fire.

— as it happens, she would *have to* wear this type of suit if she went up to high altitudes."

The boys gaped at him, and even Nita looked surprised.

"These two suits operate under entirely different principles," the doctor explained. "The first one is a partial pressure suit that operates by mechanical pressure. But it was not designed to protect women, who have a greater fluid component in their bodies than men do. The second suit is a full-pressure suit. It's really a human-shaped balloon filled with oxygen under pressure — almost like a pressurized cabin tailored to your measurements! The full-pressure suit will protect women as well as men."

Dr. Valentine went on to say that the main problems connected with designing a successful full-pressure suit were bulk, weight, heat, and lack of mobility while pressurized. The first three problems could be licked without extreme difficulty.

"That last point was a real stinker, though. Did you ever have one of those Mickey Mouse balloons with the ears? You know that if you bend one of the ears down, it'll snap right back up again because of the air pressure inside. Well, the same thing happened in the early full-pressure suits — the guy inside found himself spread-eagled as soon as the suit was inflated. For awhile, engineers thought that the suits would have to be made of articulated metal or very heavy rubber. But the problem of mobility in a pressurized suit has been solved — even though I can't tell you how!"

The doctor said that the helmet on the full-pressure suit was hard Fiberglas with a plastic foam liner. Its visor was permanently attached, and could be raised or lowered like that of a knight of old.

134

"What's the silver coverall for?" Randy asked.

"It reflects heat away from the body. You probably know that high-speed airplanes can get pretty hot inside. The suit also incorporates a ventilation garment to keep temperatures down."

"How high can you go in this suit?" Carlos asked.

"You could go into outer space in it, for a limited period. But the suit isn't really a spacesuit, because it doesn't have the facilities for long-term survival."

"But you *could* live in space, wearing this suit?"

"You could," the doctor said. "Of course, you could live in an environment that might as well be space wearing the partial-pressure suit, too. A physiologist at Wright Air Development Center made a simulated flight in an altitude chamber to 200,000 feet with the MC-3 suit. When you get that high, there are so few molecules of air left that you might as well be in space!"

"Isn't this silver suit the one the X-15 pilots wear?" Lobo asked.

"Yes. It's the most advanced suit we have. But suppose we go back closer to earth for awhile! Let's look at some of the other hazards that confront man in flight. You know that we make a special study of acceleration here at Holloman. Dr. Lundmark is going to show you our equipment a little later, so I'll let him explain g-force to you. But how about some of the less well-known perils of high flying? You'd better know about them if you plan a career in jets."

The CAP cadets learned that low atmospheric pressure sometimes resulted in decompression sickness, better known as "the bends." Nitrogen gas, they learned, is ordinarily dissolved in the bloodstream like carbon dioxide gas dissolved in a capped bottle of soda pop. Uncap the bottle, and the carbon dioxide comes out of solution because of the reduced pressure. Take a man up to very high altitude, and the nitrogen will bubble out of his blood for the same reason. The bubbles tend to collect around the joints, causing the pains known as bends. They also cause a condition known as chokes — a severe pain in the chest, together with coughing and a difficulty in breathing. A milder type of decompression sickness is called the creeps. It feels just like it sounds! The skin feels itchy, and sometimes hot or cold."

The doctor smiled reminiscently. "One time, a trainee in an altitude chamber thought he'd discovered an entirely new type of decompression sickness. He complained of a cold, wet sensation at the back of his neck! As it turned out, the chamber's air conditioning system was dripping water on him!"

The cadets laughed. Randy asked, "Can you prevent decompression sickness?"

"You can, by having the pilot breathe pure oxygen for at least an hour before ascending to 25,000 feet or more. Pre-breathing is routine for special missions that involve long stays at high altitudes without cabin pressurization."

The doctor touched briefly on some other decompression troubles — pain in ears, sinuses, abdomen and teeth, caused when entrapped gases expanded because of reduced external pressure. It was particularly important for jet pilots to have good ears and sinuses in order to avoid such troubles.

"The noise from jet engines is another problem to be coped with. You might be interested to know that a WAF major, Betsy Guild, has made significant contributions to our understanding of the effects of noise."

Another hazard faced by fliers was vertigo, or dizziness, caused by lack of aerial reference points. Vertigo

"Here's Randy dressed up for the stratosphere!"

was likely to come on when flying in fog or clouds. When flying blind without instruments, a pilot's senses would play tricks on him. He would tend to fly in an ever-tightening circle, and eventually go into a spin. The cure for vertigo involved concentrating on the navigation instruments, instead of the confusing world outside the airplane.

"How about airsickness?" asked Carlos. "That really used to floor me — then all of a sudden it seemed to disappear!"

"Motion sickness isn't too well understood. In some people, it seems to be a result of apprehension. As they get used to the new sensation of flying, the sickness disappears. Other people get sick when they ride as passengers, but not when they fly the plane themselves! We try to prevent motion sickness by keeping the flyer comfortable and relaxed. And there are several drugs that help, too."

Dr. Valentine suggested that the cadets handle and try on some of the equipment " — but not the full-pressure suit, please! I don't want the security boys hauling me off to the clink!"

Randy got hold of a standard protective helmet with mask attached, and lowered it onto his head. "Let me give you a hand with that p-hat," Dr. Valentine offered. He helped Randy fasten the strap under his chin, and showed him how the plastic sunshade visor could be lowered.

"I've got the visor down — but it won't come up!" the boy said. The doctor touched a knob on top of the hat and the visor sprang back by itself.

"How about that!" Lobo exclaimed. "Fasten the mask, Randy. There you go! Hey, guys, here's Randy all dressed up for the stratosphere! How does it feel, amigo?"

Randy unhooked the mask. "A little weird. But I

138

could get used to it mighty quick — if I just had the plane to go with it!"

The cadets stood quietly on the wind-swept desert, gazing at the high-speed sled track. Dr. Lundmark, a stocky, yellow-haired major, said, "This is the long track. It's 35,000 feet long. Its purpose is to provide an accurate measuring tool for acceleration experiments. Recording instruments placed along the track tell how fast the sled is going at a certain position. Other instruments record the stresses imposed on the sled, and whatever is inside."

"What goes inside?" Nita asked.

"This high-speed track is used mostly for testing missiles and their components, but a couple of mice rode it not too long ago. They traveled 1,100 miles an hour."

"Wow!" exclaimed one of the boys. "That's pretty good for moving on the ground."

"Let me show you something," said Dr. Lundmark mysteriously. He led the cadets a few hundred feet down the track and invited them to read a large sign stuck in the ground:

WARNING
Maximum Speed Limit
3,000 m.p.h.
Electronic Controlled

"Can the sled really go that fast?" Cactus Jack asked in a voice filled with awe.

"It sure can. The sled is propelled by a rocket booster. There are special slippers on its underside that grip the rails and prevent it from taking off."

"But — how does it stop?" Nita wondered.

"When a test is scheduled, the engineers know how

much acceleration they can expect from the rockets. They also calculate the resistance of the air. Now the tricky part comes in! Our track is designed so that the deceleration of the sled can be controlled and even varied from moment to moment. This is done by means of a water-scoop brake."

Dr. Lundmark said that the test vehicle had a scoop beneath it. During a test, the concrete trough between the track rails could be filled with varying levels of water. The water could be placed at any position along the track's length simply by moving easily penetrable portable dams. When the scoop moved down the track and plowed into a water-filled section, there was a braking effect that could be calculated. By changing the water level and the position of the water, programmed deceleration could be accomplished.

"This track can give a deceleration force of over 1,000 g's. Of course, no human being could stand such a force, but a missile might have to. During the test, all personnel retreat to a blockhouse, except for the man who fuses the boosters. He ducks into a bunker."

"Is the sled run dangerous?" Randy asked.

"Last time, we clobbered a coyote, three birds, and a skunk!"

As they climbed into the bus and headed back toward the Aeromedical Lab complex, the cadets plied Dr. Lundmark with questions about the effects of high-g.

"I've heard that you can only take five or six g's," Lobo said.

But another boy drawled, "Colonel Stapp took 40 g's on one of Holloman's tracks, didn't he, sir?"

"He did, in the historic experiments conducted in 1954. In 1958, Captain E. L. Beeding took 83 g's on our

140

Daisy track — that's a shorter one, only 120 feet long. For a fraction of a second, Captain Beeding weighed more than 11,600 pounds."

Several cadets whistled. "What happened to him?" Lobo asked.

"He went into a state of shock, but he recovered in 10 minutes. We kept him in the hospital for three days for observation, but he was able to return to work after that."

Lobo shook his head unbelievingly. "Where did I get the idea that six g's was the limit?"

"It is — in certain positions! Let me explain the factors that influence our tolerance to g-forces. The first is the rate of onset or 'jet factor.' You could continue to accelerate to millions of miles per hour if you did it gradually enough! What hurts is slamming into those g's within a short span of time.

"The second factor is the magnitude of the g's. You know that acceleration has the effect of increasing your body weight. If you weigh 200 pounds at one g, you'll weigh 2,000 pounds at 10!

"The third factor is the duration or time of exposure. Captain Beeding took the 83 g's for only a fraction of a second. He could not have stood it for a long time. The fourth factor — and here's where you come in, Lobo — is the *direction* in which the g-force is applied."

The doctor explained that human anatomy would tolerate acceleration better in certain positions than it would in others. The head-to-toe limit was 6 g's. The toe-to-head limit was only 3.

"The men who have survived very high g's have had them applied transversely — through the body. They've been incapacitated by the force, but they've lived through it."

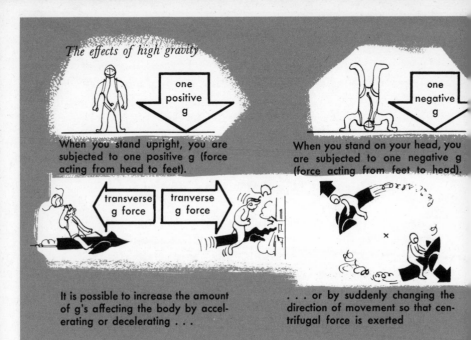

The effects of high gravity

When you stand upright, you are subjected to one positive g (force acting from head to feet).

When you stand on your head, you are subjected to one negative g (force acting from feet to head).

It is possible to increase the amount of g's affecting the body by accelerating or decelerating . . .

. . . or by suddenly changing the direction of movement so that centrifugal force is exerted

"What's a practical transverse-g load?" Major Bullock asked.

"About 17 to 20 g's for 20 seconds. Here we are at the Daisy! Would you like to look her over?"

The cadets and Major Bullock climbed out. They found the Daisy track behind one of the buildings. It was 120 feet long, and had a seat mounted on its sled.

"Daisy can duplicate every effect of the long track except wind-blast and high rocket sled speed. And of course, it can't produce long-term g's."

The cadets inspected the seat somewhat apprehensively. Nita said, "I should think it'd have a windscreen in front."

"Nope," smiled Dr. Lundmark. "You ride backwards!"

The aviation medicine specialist explained that they

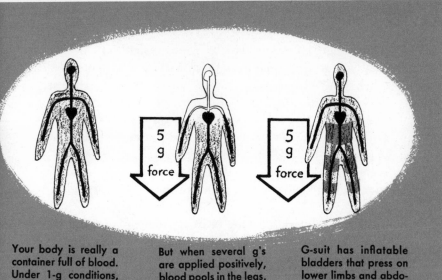

Your body is really a container full of blood. Under 1-g conditions, the heart can pump blood to all parts of the body.

But when several g's are applied positively, blood pools in the legs, leaves brain, causes blackout.

G-suit has inflatable bladders that press on lower limbs and abdomen, prevent blood pooling and blackout.

had learned that front-to-back g's could be tolerated best of all. And so the high-g runs were made with the rider facing toward the rear. The high gravity was produced by the abrupt deceleration of the sled when it struck a water cylinder at the end of the track.

"But I thought we were talking about acceleration — not deceleration!" said one of the cadets.

"We call speeding up acceleration and slowing down deceleration. But they both result in the same kind of stresses on the body."

"How do g's hit a guy flying a jet?" Randy asked.

"Flyers pull g's when they go into tight turns, or loop, or pull out of a dive. At 2 g's, you feel as though an invisible giant were sitting on you. At 3, you usually can't lift your arms or legs; your face skin sags down — and that p-hat weighs much too much! Your eyesight will begin to gray out around the edges then, and at 4 to 5 g's you'll black out. You're not unconscious, but you can't see. Above 5 g's, you lose consciousness. Tense pilots last longer than relaxed ones, because you can tolerate more g's under conditions of nervous and muscular tension.

"You probably know that the g-suit was developed to increase g-tolerance. To understand how it works, you have to know what goes on inside the body when g's are applied."

Dr. Lundmark said that ordinary plane maneuvers produced head-to-toe g's. The effect was as though someone grabbed the pilot by his hair and swung him rapidly around and around — the blood rushed to his feet. When the blood pressure in his brain fell below a certain point, consciousness was lost. G-suits had inflatable bladders at the abdomen, thighs, and lower legs. When the force of acceleration exceeded 2 g's, the bladders automatically inflated, preventing the blood from becoming pooled in the lower body. The suit applied more pressure as the g-force mounted, and released the pressure as the force subsided.

"Pilots can wear a separate g-suit incorporated in a coverall-type flying suit, or they can wear the MC-4 pressure suit that has a g-suit built right in.

As the cadets inspected the other facilities at Holloman, they learned that much of the work determining the human tolerance limits to g-force had been done here. More testing was in progress. The aim of the scientists was to make man capable of standing any g-load that his airplane could. As ships traveled many times the speed of sound, they became capable of inflicting higher and higher g-loads on the men riding inside. The rocket ship that carried man beyond earth's atmosphere would produce the heaviest g-load of all.

"How many g's do you think we could pull in this old gooney-bird, sir?" Carlos asked Major Bullock at the end of the day, as the Cornudo Squadron reboarded their faithful C-47.

"Not very many," smiled Major Bullock. "How about it, cadets? Now that you know the perils of supersonic jet flight, are you ready to settle for something more easy going?"

Nita and the boys responded with a single yell:

"No!"

The major sighed. "That's what I was afraid of."

CHAPTER EIGHT

REDCAP!

"YOU'RE DOING FINE, RANDY! Just keep it cool!" Beads of perspiration stood out on the boy's forehead, and the back of his shirt was soaked. Was it because of the heat, which had turned the range below into a tinder-dry expanse of brown waste? Or was it because Randy was just about to enter the final leg of landing the Cessna?

"You're settling fine," Uncle Glarfie said. "Relax, and watch those wings. We don't want any Chinese landings! You know — Won Wing Low!"

But Randy couldn't laugh. The ground seemed to rise up with great speed. He exerted all of his skill to level the ship and keep her in the air. A little back pressure on the

146

wheel increased the angle of attack and slowed the plane at an altitude of about 10 feet. The ship settled smoothly, and Randy felt the wheels touch the rock-hard soil of the airstrip. He relaxed the back pressure. The nose wheel met the ground.

Down the strip, next to the hanger, Randy could see three figures. One of them was jumping up and down and waving his arms wildly.

"Look at that Sam," Randy remarked amusedly to his uncle. "You'd think *he* landed the plane." But the boy's heart warmed to the enthusiasm of his younger brother. Good old Sam was in there cheering.

When the ship rolled to a final stop in front of the hanger, Sam and Mr. and Mrs. Murrow crowded close to congratulate Randy.

"That was a fine two-man solo," Mr. Morrow said.

"He didn't need me in there with him," Uncle Glarfie said. "I just went along for the free ride."

Randy disagreed. "Look — I just took off the plane, flew it around a little bit, and landed it. But I'm not ready to solo it yet! Not by a long shot!"

"I'm proud of you anyway, son," Mrs. Morrow said. "You'll make a fine airman."

"How about it, Randy?" his father asked, as they started for the ranch jeep. "Are you still planning to be a jet pilot?"

"I don't know, Dad," the boy said honestly. "Maybe I could tell if somebody'd let me fly a jet!"

Uncle Glarfie whistled. "That's a tall order. But if you continue to do so well in your CAP work, you might become eligible for the jet orientation course."

And what a wonderful experience that would be, the boy thought. During the course, CAP cadets spent nine days at an Air Force Base with the status of student officers.

They were familiarized with jet aircraft and issued flying equipment. After being trained in the use of oxygen and seat ejection equipment, they were taken for their first jet ride. The cadet was permitted to take the controls. On subsequent days, the cadet progressed as far as he was able toward mastering the intricacies of jet flight. He plotted courses, made cross-country flights, and between times devoured all of the technical manuals he could get hold of. The purpose of the course was to introduce the cadet to jet aviation. Some cadets who had taken the jet orientation course became members of the Air Force. Others went on to become aeronautical engineers.

But I'm still not old enough, Randy though sorrowfully. Major Bullock had told him that, to be eligible for the jet orientation, a boy would have to be ready to graduate from high school. From where he stood now, Randy thought that two years was going to pass mighty slowly!

"There goes another airplane," Sam remarked, breaking the thread of Randy's daydream. The jeep riders looked up.

"That's Cavanaugh's old Cub," said Uncle Glarfie thoughtfully. "Now what do you suppose he's doing over in these parts at this time of day?"

The jeep turned into the main ranchhouse yard. Then Uncle Glarfie slammed on the brakes as they very nearly collided with the pickup truck. Carlos at the wheel, it came careening around the corner of a shed and swerved to a halt.

"Confound it, Carlos — " the rancher blazed.

"Dad! For heaven's sake save it! There's a REDCAP on!"

Mr. Morrow frowned. "What is it, Glar?"

"There's a plane missing, and the CAP is starting a

148

search operation. They'll be setting up a search base at the Cornudo Airport."

Carlos exclaimed impatiently, "Let's go! Come on, Randy!"

"See you later," Randy said, leaping out of the jeep. His uncle followed to the truck, and in a moment they were on their way back to the airstrip.

"Now we know why Cavanaugh was heading west in the Cub," the cattleman said grimly. "They'll be calling every pilot in the area. Any idea what kind of plane is down, Carlos?"

"We got the word from Kirtland Air Force Base. It's a T-bird on a cross-country from Oxnard, California, to Lowry in Colorado. Reported engine trouble this side of Las Vegas, and not another squeak out of him."

The truck came to a ramming halt and the three of them dashed for the Cessna. As they waited for the fuel tanks to fill, Uncle Glarfie rummaged in the chart compartment and came up with a sheet unlike any Randy had ever seen. It was marked SOUTHWEST — ENROUTE HIGH ALTITUDE.

"Look, Randy. Here's the jet-victor airway he must have been following." The rancher's finger traced a line labeled J-13-V leading from Las Vegas to Pueblo, Colorado. "You know," the man added, "this is not country that *I* would care to be down in!"

Things were under control at the Cornudo Airport when the Cessna landed. In the CAP building, a board had been set up. Nita was busily chalking information on it concerning the ships taking part in the search mission. There were six aircraft out already.

"Mr. Cavanaugh is waiting for an observer, Randy. Get your grid assignment from Mrs. Wilkins." I suppose you'll be taking Carlos as your observer, Mr. Haines?"

High-altitude navigation chart

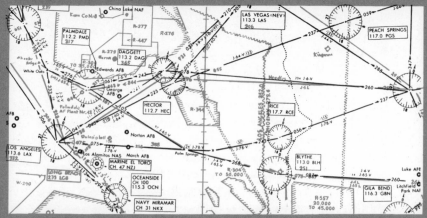

High-flying jets do not need charts that show extensive surface features. They fly by radio, not by visual reference. Notice the omni-range Jet Victor airways (J-3-V) and the low-frequency/medium-frequency routes. (J-3-L). A third type of navigation facility, TACAN, has its routes indicated by J-O-T (not shown).

Randy moved over to the desk where white-haired Mrs. Wilkins sat, working over two charts. Randy greeted the retired schoolteacher and requested an area to search.

"You'll fly grid 12, Randy. Good luck."

Randy marked out the area on a large-scale survey map, picked up a pair of binoculars, and headed for Mr. Cavanaugh's Cub.

"She's gassed and ready, boy!" the old man called. He wore a faded cotton shirt and skin-tight levis. His Stetson was ancient and curled up on both sides, and his chin bore a wintry stubble of white. The airplane seemed as ancient as its owner, and in the back of his mind Randy hoped that they would not find themselves the object of a search before the mission was over.

"Here're the charts, Mr. Cavanaugh. I'll prop her for you, if you like."

150

The old man climbed into the cabin. Randy called, "Switch off?"

"Off!"

Randy turned the propeller to prime the engine, then called, "Contact!"

"Contact!" yelled Mr. Cavanaugh, and Randy snapped the prop through. The engine sputtered to life, and the boy ran around and climbed in. In a few minutes, they left the airport far behind.

As observer, it was Randy's job to navigate the plane and search the ground for signs of the lost aircraft or its pilot. Mr. Cavanaugh concentrated on flying the Cub at an altitude of only 500 feet, flying in a pattern over the grid area that had been assigned to them.

"Not very pretty country, is it, Mr. Cavanaugh?" Randy remarked as he began to scrutinize the brown plateau beneath.

"It'll blossom, come spring. You don't see the Southwest at her best in September."

Randy gave a start. "Look there at two o'clock! The other side of that dry wash!"

"An airplane," the old man muttered. "Doesn't look like a jet, though. Let's take a closer look."

The Cub dived. As they flew over the spot Randy had indicated, the boy gave a groan. He had spotted a large yellow X painted on one wing of the wreck beneath. "An old wreck! Back to the grid, Mr. Cavanaugh!"

They resumed the tedious search, flying up and down the plateau until the Cub's gas grew low. Then they flew back to Cornudo.

Mrs. Wilkins came running out to meet them as they taxied up to a gasoline truck. "The State Police received a phone call from Cherryvale. Someone reported a jet flying very low!"

151

"Cherryvale?" Mr. Cavanaugh tipped his Stetson forward and scratched his gray pate. "That's way east of where the jet should've been. Must be a mistake."

Mrs. Wilkins looked determined. "Nonetheless, I'm assigning you to a grid over in those parts. Here's the map, Randy."

"This will be a wild goose chase," the old man muttered.

"You hurry up, Rafe Cavanaugh," Mrs. Wilkins scolded, "or you won't have enough daylight to finish your grid!"

"Yes'm," said the cowman meekly. Randy smiled, but wisely said nothing. When the Cub was pronounced ready by the cadets of the ground crew, Randy swung the prop and they were off.

Cherryvale was northeast of Cornudo. They began the careful grid-flying procedure once more, working their way slowly eastward from the little settlement.

"We go much farther, we'll end up over Canyon Largo," Mr. Cavanaugh said.

Randy did not remove his eyes from the binoculars.

The old man persisted. "There's going to be tricky air currents over the canyon this late in the afternoon, and this old ship doesn't have all the power in the world. Randy — I don't think it'd be wise to keep on this grid. HQ can assign another plane to it, while we stay over the plateau."

The boy sighed. "It's your ship, Mr. Cavanaugh. We've almost finished combing our assigned area anyhow. Hey — *wait a minute!*"

For a breathless span of time, Randy plied the binoculars. "Please, Mr. Cavanaugh! Fly toward that arm of the canyon. I'm sure I see smoke!"

152

"Some camper cookin' up his chuck," the old man grumbled. But he sent the Cub winging over the escarpment toward the cleft in the rock Randy had pointed out. The brush in the canyon arm was on fire. Randy swept the powerful glasses toward the upwind end of the charred area.

"It's the jet," he said quietly.

"Take the stick and let me look." Randy held the wallowing little airplane steady while Mr. Cavanaugh used the binoculars. "You're right, boy. She crashed on the slope, belly down with both wings broke off. Canopy's gone, so the pilot must have ejected."

"I'll radio the base," Randy said. He picked up the little hand mike and sent out a call for Cornudo.

"You'd better wait'll we get some altitude, or that call won't even get out of the canyon!" the old man said testily. He moved the throttle of the Cub to full on, and the plane obediently began to climb.

"CAP radio," said the receiver.

"This is Piper seven-seven-four-two-bravo. We have located the strike in Canyon Largo, southwest quadrant of grid 31. There is no sign of the pilot. He seems to have ejected. Over."

"Roger, four-two-bravo. Can you orbit? Over."

"We have fuel for one-half hour. Over."

"Roger, four-two-bravo. We are dispatching aircraft to strike area. Continue to orbit until their arrival."

"Roger, CAP. Piper four-two-bravo out."

"CAP radio."

Randy hung up the microphone. "Now we go round and round until the others get here."

"Randy, boy — I've got other plans!"

"I don't understand."

"It's the jet!"

The old man hunched his thin shoulders impatiently. "Get those binoculars out again. We'll stay in the area to guide the other ships in — but we're going to continue our search! What good is the crashed jet? What we want to find is the pilot! Now put on your thinking cap and figure where he might have drifted."

Randy tried to consider all of the factors. They could see that the jet had been heading almost due east when it crashed. But the north wind would have carried a parachutist toward the opposite side of the canyon. "Of course, he *could* have ejected earlier, over the plateau."

"Don't be stupid, boy! We just combed that area! He's got to be in the canyon!"

Randy flushed with embarassment at the old man's blunt talk. But he had to admit that Mr. Cavanaugh was right. The Cub continued to labor upward as the boy scanned the terraced rocks below.

"We'll get over near the other rim," said the old man sending the Cub into a climbing turn. Keep looking!"

The ship moved closer and closer to the bleak face of the canyon wall. There were occasional level places where rockfalls had softened the forbidding craggy palisade, and on one of these Randy spotted something white.

"Let's get between those two big hunks of rock. This could be it!"

The Cub spiraled downward once more. "It's a chute. I'm sure of it! But what a place to be down in. . . ."

The Cub was drifting closer and closer to the canon's downwind wall. Suddenly the plane reared back and upwards, caught in a powerful updraft. With an oath, Mr. Cavanaugh applied power and tried to force the ship back into a semblance of control. But before he could level the ship, another air current caught it and sent it lurching downward in a sickening spiral dive.

"Sweet mother! We'll fall apart!" the old man yelled, but before he could take any action at all, the ship was flung upward again. The next minutes were a nightmare. Randy clutched the sides of his seat as the plane seemed to toss in the air like a leaf. Then — almost abruptly, it seemed — they were in a calm glide.

Heading straight for the canyon wall!

"Mr. Cavanaugh! For Pete's sake!"

"Calm down, boy," said the old man dryly. "The engine's out. We'll have to try to land her on that slope where you spotted the parachute."

The only noise was the whistling of the wind on the flanks of the Cub. She shuddered and bounced in the rough air, then banked toward the small, boulder-strewn area.

"Get braced," Mr. Cavanaugh sang out. The Cub's nose went up and Randy felt the tail whack into the ground. There was a great crunching sound and an almost unbearable jar — then silence.

"Are you — all right, Mr. Cavanaugh?"

There was no answer. The boy unfastened his seat belt and crept forward to the seat where the old man was. Mr. Cavanaugh's head was thrown back, and his eyes were closed. The seamed face was pale and shrunken about the lips and nose.

Oh, no Randy thought. But a feeble movement of the bony chest told him that the old man was alive.

With great care, Randy opened the battered airplane door and began to extricate the unconscious occupant of the front seat. The Cub had come to rest in a rough heap of boulders near the foot of a gigantic rock. There was very little light left. When Randy had the old man clear of the plane, he hurried back to retrieve the survival gear which he knew should be behind his seat.

The next minutes were a nightmare.

A few minutes later, he sat on the rocky ground and contemplated the rotten luck that had marooned him with useful survival equipment consisting of a canteen of warm water, a length of nylon rope, and a three-cell flashlight. To this he could add a pocket knife and a book of matches.

"Why couldn't you have put in a little food?" Randy asked the silent figure lying beside him. "And a blanket? I don't even have anything to cover you up with."

He decided to make a fire, with the dual purpose of warming the unconscious man and indicating their position to rescuers. But the only burnable material available was prickly scrub that tore his hands and stubbornly resisted any effort to break it. Finally, by chopping at it with his knife, he obtained a small pile. It gave a meager, smoky fire. But with this as a beacon, Randy felt it was safe to range out a little. He took the rope and the flashlight and began to work his way cautiously toward the place where he judged the parachute would be.

"Anybody here?" he called. His voice echoed back eerily from the rocks. The only other sound was the rattle of the stones dislodged by his feet. Doggedly, he kept moving. The tiny beacon fire dwindled to a fitful spark. I don't dare go much further, he thought. If I lose that fire, I won't get back to Mr. Cavanaugh before morning!

And then the beam of his flashlight struck something that gleamed soft white. The chute! The light picked up a shroud line and followed it into a hollow full of sharp rocks. There was a figure there.

Randy rushed over the rough ground and shined his light into the hollow. The pilot's body had probably been dragged here by the chute. Randy slid carefully downward and moved closer. The man's face was com-

The man's face was completely hidden.

kit's lightweight folding rifle, Ra

The boy decided that he wou
Cavanaugh to this spot. It was sl
which had begun to rise, and
prickly brush nearby that could b

The survival kit contained a li
lit this and set it on a prominent
to the site of the Cub crash.

He found the old man still
breathing seemed deeper and steadi
thought, hoisting the wiry little fr
a fireman's carry. He was heavier t
heavier!

"I'll never make it with him!'
muscles seemed ready to snap und
barely half of the distance had been
put him down — I'll never get him

He knew that it would be imp
Cavanaugh all the way to the hollow.
to that next rock," he said to himse
promised that he would carry the ol
mesquite bush. At the bush, he the
able to make it to a crag a few rod
that point, he found that he was near
red light.

Randy's back refused to straighten
after he had reached his destinatic
Cavanaugh beside the pilot. "A guy li
bad shape," the boy said aloud, "whe
himself to get a job done!" But his
now secure together. Randy covered the
silk of the parachute, then took the m
he had found in the survival kit and be
brush.

T
desol
durin
for t
The
fire

knew
50 d
until
lit
thro

not
heli
thro

pletely hidden by helmet, visor, and mask. A dark, moist stain had spread over one leg of his summer flying suit.

Randy reached an unsteady hand toward the helmet visor. It flew up, revealing the closed eyes beneath. Randy's gaze dimmed — then cleared as he gave a violent start.

The eyes had opened!

They were looking at him.

"Who are you?" came a muffled, very faint voice. Randy hastened to unhook the mask.

"CAP — air rescue —" the boy said.

"You," the pilot observed in an accusing tone, "are late. I intend . . . to complain . . . to the management." His eyes closed and his head lolled forward. But Randy knew he was still alive. He unfastened the parachute harness and removed the pilot's helmet. Then he looked at the injured leg.

Randy had had enough first aid to know what a compound fracture was. He sliced open the fabric of the suit leg and saw that blood was still welling slowly from the wound.

Must be a vein, he thought. The pilot was alive, but he wouldn't be for long unless that bleeding was stopped. Randy took off his own uniform shirt and cut it into strips, which he bound firmly around the injured leg. Then he bundled up the parachute silk into a makeshift couch and eased the pilot onto it. When the man was free of his parachute harness, Randy noticed the seat pack.

"A survival kit!" he exclaimed, hurriedly unzipping the canvas container. He laid out the contents, then seized the first-aid kit. It contained sulfa, which Randy dusted over the wound. Then, using bandages and the

159

The man's face was completely hidden.

kit's lightweight folding rifle, Randy improvised a splint.

The boy decided that he would attempt to bring Mr. Cavanaugh to this spot. It was sheltered from the wind, which had begun to rise, and there was more of the prickly brush nearby that could be used as fuel for a fire.

The survival kit contained a little signal light. Randy lit this and set it on a prominent rock, then started back to the site of the Cub crash.

He found the old man still unconscious, but his breathing seemed deeper and steadier. *Upsy daisy,* Randy thought, hoisting the wiry little frame onto his back in a fireman's carry. He was heavier than he looked. *Much* heavier!

"I'll never make it with him!" The boy's tortured muscles seemed ready to snap under the strain, when barely half of the distance had been traversed. "But if I put him down — I'll never get him back up again."

He knew that it would be impossible to carry Mr. Cavanaugh all the way to the hollow. "I'll just bring him to that next rock," he said to himself. At the rock, he promised that he would carry the old man only to the mesquite bush. At the bush, he thought he might be able to make it to a crag a few rods beyond — and at that point, he found that he was nearly back to the little red light.

Randy's back refused to straighten for several minutes after he had reached his destination and laid Mr. Cavanaugh beside the pilot. "A guy like me is in pretty bad shape," the boy said aloud, "when he has to trick himself to get a job done!" But his two charges were now secure together. Randy covered them with the ample silk of the parachute, then took the miniature axe that he had found in the survival kit and began stiffly to cut brush.

161

The moon came over the canyon rim, washing the desolation with pale, cheerless light. At several times during his makeshift rescue operations, Randy listened for the sound of search planes. But the night was silent. The search would be called off until morning. A beacon fire would be to no avail.

But they *do* need warmth, Randy said to himself. He knew that temperatures in these areas sometimes dropped 50 degrees between sunset and sunrise. So he cut brush until his hands were too raw to hold the little axe, then lit his fire and kept feeding it with the spiny branches through the long night.

When dawn finally came, he was far too sleepy to notice it. And he never even saw the big Air Force helicopter that came with the dawn and carried the three of them away.

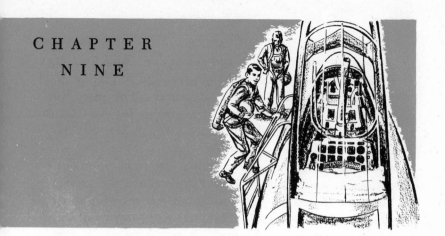

CHAPTER NINE

THE OPENING SKIES

THE EVENTS THAT FOLLOWED had seemed almost like a dream to Randy. He awoke in the hospital at Las Vegas feeling rested and ready for action, and it wasn't until he threw the blankets back and sprang out of bed that he discovered the mittenlike bandages on his .hands. They made it impossible to ring for the nurse, so he went wandering down the corridors in his pajamas until they found him and made him go back under protest.

Then there had been a meeting with his parents and Sam, together with the Haineses, which produced some uncalled-for sentimentality on the part of the ladies, and rather embarrassing compliments from the men.

Major Bullock and most of the rest of the CAP squadron had also come to the hospital. And from them Randy learned that both Mr. Cavanaugh and the jet pilot, Lt. Blaine, were expected to recover. The pilot would rejoin his group as soon as his broken leg healed. But poor Mr. Cavanaugh's heart attack had put an end to his flying days.

The delegation of Air Force brass had been quite a surprise, and Randy was still hazy about the replies he gave to the dapper little one-star general who asked so many questions about Randy's plans for the future. Looking back on the episode, Randy came to the conclusion that the general was probably responsible for what happened after that.

The letter came to Randy in care of the Flying X, arriving on the day before the Morrows planned to return home to Chicago. It was on the letterhead of the Department of the Air Force. And even now, as he sat in the C-119 winging toward Dayton, Randy could remember fragments of its phrasing . . . *in appreciation of your extraordinary action . . . undoubtedly saving the life of Lt. Paul Blaine . . . the Air Force is honored to extend this invitation . . . visit the facilities of Wright Air Development Center, Ohio, largest center of the Air Research and Development Command . . .*

"You lucky guy!" Carlos had exlaimed. "Be sure to see the supersonic wind tunnel and the combustion chambers where they test jet fuel mixtures!"

"And the man-carrying centrifuge and the vertical accelerator and the room that roasts you on one side and freezes you on the other," Lobo added.

"And the weightless airplane!" said Cactus Jack. "Write to us and tell us all about everything."

"Better yet," Nita said, "come back to New Mexico next summer and give us the word in person!"

There had been good-byes and good wishes, and then a flight home from Albuquerque. His summer with the Cornudo squadron had come to an end, but he found that his own city held an enthusiastic CAP group that welcomed him gladly.

And then the day had come to visit Wright. The C-119 delivered its load of cargo, plus one CAP cadet named Randy Morrow, to the sprawling network of laboratories, test stands and runways that now covered the site of the Wright Brothers' early experiments.

Randy's guide met him at the airfield. "Captain Holly! What are you doing here?"

"I'm assigned here temporarily on a research project. When I heard about your visit, I decided I knew just the man to be your guide."

"That sounds swell!"

"You're in for a busy two days, Randy! Did they tell you what to expect?"

"I've been wandering in a rosy fog ever since I got the invitation!"

"Well, come out into the blue sky department, and let me show you some of the ways you can make a career out of jet aircraft."

And so Randy began his tour of the vast establishment. He started by visiting the engineering test facilities. He stood in the gaping maw of a gigantic wind tunnel and watched aerodynamic engineers prepare a full-scale model for stability experiments. In the unusual 12-foot vertical wind tunnel, he himself launched a model and watched it recover from an artificially induced spin.

He spoke with the men who had designed the ejection

materials research

rocket engine research

communications research

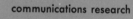

aerodynamic research

propulsion research

Wright Brothers Memorial

space medicine

electronics research

optics research

seats used in every military jet, and examined models of the strange "escape capsules" — whole cabins that broke away and parachuted to earth — that would eventually solve the problem of supersonic ejection.

In a steel and reinforced concrete test building of the fluid dynamics branch, he saw engineers conducting basic research into the combustion of fuels in jet and rocket engines. He saw ramjet test stands for simulating speeds of Mach 4 at 100,000 feet, and turbojet stands capable of testing engines up to 60,000 pounds thrust.

In the materials testing labs, he saw scientists investigating new lubricants that would retain their efficiency at high temperatures. He saw a sample of "cermet," the strange blend of metal and ceramic which was being developed as a non-melting engine lining. He saw tests being conducted on titanium aircraft skins that resisted the high temperatures encountered at speeds beyond Mach 2.

Electronic and mechanical engineers were at work on new control systems that would enable human pilots to keep a bridle on their supersonic steeds. In cases where the reactions of the pilot were too slow for the airplane, new computers took over some of the duties of the human being.

Captain Holly was quick to affirm that man was not obsolete, however. No computer could substitute for him in situations that called for judgment. It was the job of Wright 'human factors' scientists to provide equipment that would keep man healthy and reasonably comfortable under the conditions encountered during high-speed flight.

Randy saw the whirling centrifuge that could be used to simulate prolonged periods of high acceleration. He saw a model of a weightlessness simulator which would enable physiologists and psychologists to study the effect of zero-gravity. Deep in the basement of a psychology building, he saw a dark, silent chamber where volunteers would sit for hours so that Air Force doctors could obtain basic data on the behavior of humans under unusual conditions. In another building, he saw a bewilderingly varied zoo of experimental animals, who would provide some of the answers that man must have before he traveled safely into the depths of outer space itself.

As the morning of the second day drew to a close, Captain Holly said casually, "So far, you've had a rather objective look at the world of jet aircraft, haven't you."

"Why, yes, I suppose I have," the boy replied cautiously.

"How'd you like to be *subjective* about things? Really experience some of the things we've seen being analyzed and developed?"

Randy took a deep breath and said, "If you're asking me if I'd like to ride in a jet, the answer is *YES!*"

"Then come along with me to the flight line and we'll pick out a trainer nobody's using at the moment."

"Here is a faithful old T-bird, Randy — a T-33A. The first operational jet trainer."

Randy touched the aluminum skin gently. "I know that she must seem tame to *you*, Captain—after flying 102's and 104's — but right now, she looks like the prettiest ship in the world!"

"Ah," the pilot said wisely. "But wait until you fly her! Have you ever flown a plane, Randy?"

"I had about 12 hours in a Cessna 175."

"This will be quite a change. Let's get our equipment."

They collected parachutes, p-hats, and oxygen masks

169

from the personal equipment room. A technician fitted Randy, testing his mask for leaks and making sure that his mike and headset connections were working.

Then the test pilot and the boy went back to the flight line. The ground crew chief and his men were getting the ship ready. Randy watched Captain Holly check the airplane carefully himself, using a much more elaborate version of the line check Randy had used on his uncle's light plane. When he was satisfied that the T-bird was in good shape. Captain Holly invited Randy to climb the ladder and be seated in the aft cockpit.

"I'll explain the ejection seat as I get you fastened in, Randy. The two yellow handles at the front actuate the seat. To blast off, you first pull up the left handle. That will blow the canopy if I haven't already done it. Then pull up the right handle to arm the seat. Then squeeze this trigger on the right handle — and away you go."

"That's all I have to do?"

"That's all. Your seat belt opens automatically to release you from the seat, and your parachute opens automatically at the proper altitude. This little gizmo here is called a zero clip. I'll attach it now, and once we're airborne I'll tell you to detach it. Its only purpose is to open the chute and lap belt instantly if we have to eject at a very low altitude."

"I've got it, "Randy said.

"You look pretty cool about sitting on a cannon cracker!" the pilot laughed. "Well — the only other thing you have to know about the seat is how to arm it. It has three safety pins that are inserted on the right side to prevent accidental firing while the ship is on the ground.

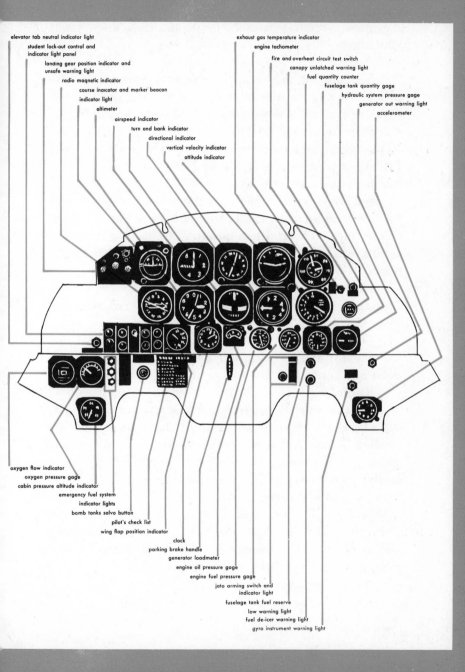

elevator tab neutral indicator light
student lock-out control and
indicator light panel
landing gear position indicator and
unsafe warning light
radio magnetic indicator
course indicator and marker beacon
indicator light
altimeter
airspeed indicator
turn and bank indicator
directional indicator
vertical velocity indicator
attitude indicator

exhaust gas temperature indicator
engine tachometer
fire and overheat circuit test switch
canopy unlatched warning light
fuel quantity counter
fuselage tank quantity gage
hydraulic system pressure gage
generator out warning light
accelerometer

oxygen flow indicator
oxygen pressure gage
cabin pressure altitude indicator
emergency fuel system
indicator lights
bomb tanks salvo button
pilot's check list
wing flap position indicator
clock
parking brake handle
generator loadmeter
engine oil pressure gage
engine fuel pressure gage
jato arming switch and
indicator light
fuselage tank fuel reserve
low warning light
fuel de-icer warning light
gyro instrument warning light

To remove them, you push, twist, and pull when I tell you to."

"Roger!"

The hose of the oxygen mask was fastened to the plane's system, and also secured on the parachute harness. "We have to tie it down so that it doesn't smack you in the chops if we eject. The hose has a quick-disconnect — but sometimes it doesn't disconnect quickly enough! I'll adjust your regulator for you, and you can hook on the mask when we're ready to roll."

Captain Holly climbed into the forward cockpit, and the crewmen attached cables from a booster battery truck to the ship. Within a few minutes, Randy heard the jet engine whine to a start. He fastened his mask and got ready to obey the pilot's orders.

"Remove your pins, Randy."

Randy removed them and held up the red streamer that they were attached to.

"I'd like you to hold the stick in your right hand and the throttle in your left while we take off. Don't exert any control — just follow through with me."

"Roger."

The canopy was lowered until it was almost closed, and the ship began to taxi toward the runway. In his headset, Randy heard the instructions from the control tower. They were given permission to take off. Captain Holly locked the canopy, moved the ship into the assigned runway, and began the takeoff run.

See how she runs, said a little voice in the back of Randy's brain. *And runs—and runs!* What a lot of space she needed to take off in. But once the ship was off the ground, how powerfully she climbed!

"Detach the zero clip, Randy."

"Roger."

Randy studied the panel of instruments before him, and found that they were not quite so confusing as they looked. There were quite a few unfamiliar ones, but the six flight instruments he needed most were right in the center. He saw the altimeter wind up to 17,000 before the ship leveled off.

"Here we are, Randy. Are you ready to take over?"

"Whenever you want to give her to me."

"She's all yours."

The boy gripped the stick firmly. "Can you give me a hint on turn and bank?" he asked.

"Forget the rudder," Captain Holly advised. "And be gentle."

Randy eased the plane into a bank. *Why, it's effortless!* he thought. *Just the lightest touch moves her!* But the nose was down, just the way he goofed in the beginning with the Cessna! He leveled off, then banked again. This time the little plane inside the attitude indicator kept its nose on the level. Up forward, Captain Holly raised his hand in an "okay" signal, and Randy felt a thrill of pride. He repeated the maneuver in several variations, then said, "Will you show me some aerobatics?"

"All right. Keep your hands on the stick and throttle."

The ship did snap rolls. It performed inside loops, one after another, and did barrel rolls and peel-offs. It dived and pulled g's.

"Holy Moses!" Randy said. The test pilot chuckled.

"Will you do that again, and show me where the accelerometer is first?"

"Down on the far right. Watch it as we pull out of the dive."

When the maneuver was over, Randy sounded somewhat disappointed. "It sure felt like it ought to be more than just two g's."

The ship was a part of him.

"Only because the sensation is unfamiliar, Randy. Jets are *different*. Their smooth response and power just have no equal among piston planes. You don't realize you're traveling so fast until you try a maneuver like a dive pull-out. *Then* you know! There are a lot of pleasant little surprises about jets. You don't have to worry about propeller torque. And the trim is electric! See the little gizmos on the top and side of the stick? Like rubber sea shells? They trim her."

Randy took the controls again, and for a long, silent time, he simply *flew*. Finally he said, "I thought that the high speed and power would make the ship hard to handle. But that's not true at all! You have to take the speed into consideration when you're planning your turns and pulling out of dives — but after awhile you just think jet!"

"Great, isn't it?" asked the pilot.

"I'll say." The boy eased the jet into a shallow climbing turn. Here he was, strapped and plugged firmly into the ship; but he didn't feel like one of its components.

Instead, the ship was a part of him! Controlling it required no more effort than controlling one of his own legs. And that's what a jet plane was, he decided: the longest legs in the world.

The ship soared higher and higher. If only, he thought, it could keep going forever!

The End